Home Electrics

Home
Electrics

Geoffrey Burdett

Newnes Technical Books

The Butterworth Group

UNITED KINGDOM

Butterworth & Co (Publishers) Ltd
London: 88 Kingsway, WC2B 6 AB

AUSTRALIA

Butterworths Pty Ltd
Sydney: 586 Pacific Highway, Chatswood NSW 2067
Also at Melbourne, Brisbane, Adelaide and Perth

CANADA

Butterworth & Co (Canada) Ltd
Toronto: 2265 Midland Avenue, Scarborough,
Ontario, M1P 4S1

NEW ZEALAND

Butterworths of New Zealand Ltd
Wellington: T & W Young Building,
77—85 Customhouse Quay, 1, CPO Box 472

SOUTH AFRICA

Butterworth & Co (South Africa) (Pty) Ltd
Durban: 152—154 Gale Street

USA

Butterworth (Publishers) Inc
Boston: 10 Tower Office Park, Woburn, Mass 01801, USA

First published 1977 by Newnes Technical Books
     Reprinted 1978, 1980

ISBN 0 408 00245 X

Printed in England by Butler & Tanner Ltd.,
Frome and London

Preface

A home will not look after itself, and the occupant must prepared to do battle with damp, rust and corrosion, fading, peeling, wormholes, leaks, blown fuses— and much more besides.

Of course you can call in a man, but with so much of the work labour-intensive— the areas where costs are now so very high—you will have to delve deep in your pocket to keep up with the bills. From this stems the great incentive to tackle the work yourself; if you can reduce costs to materials only, this will have two immediate effects. First, you will have money to do more and, secondly, you may have money available with which to buy better quality materials and add the frills.

The term do-it-yourself encompasses a very wide field of activity, and there is much to learn. It is not always easy, but once new skills have been mastered d-i-y becomes rewarding and satisfying. The books in this new series which as well as plumbing cover subjects ranging from electric wiring cover subjects ranging from decorating and plumbing to heating, are designed to help you acquire the necessary skills. All you need to add is practice!

They are written by people with very considerable practical experience in the d-i-y field, and all have been involved in feature-writing for DIY magazine over the years. The authors have also been responsible for dealing with hundreds of readers' queries—which has given them an invaluable insight into the problems encountered in and about the house.

I'm sure you will find their advice invaluable. May I wish you success in all you undertake.

Tony Wilkins,
Editor, Do-it-yourself Magazine

Acknowledgements

The author and publishers would like to thank the following firms for their help in supplying information and illustrations relating to their products.

AMF-Venner Ltd.
Ashley Accessories Ltd.
Belling & Co Ltd.
BSR (Housewares) Ltd.
BICC Ltd.
E. Chidlow & Co Ltd.
Concord Lighting International Ltd.
J. A. Crabtree & Co Ltd.
Creda Electric Ltd.
Duraplug.
Egatube Ltd.
Electrical Association for Women.
Electricity Council.
Fotherby Willis Electronics Ltd.
Home Automation Ltd.
Humex Ltd.
Lewdon Metal Products Ltd.
Maclamp Co Ltd.
M.E.M. Ltd.
MK Electric Ltd.
Nettle Accessories Ltd.
Osram-GEC Ltd.
Ottermill Switchgear Ltd.
Philips Electrical Ltd.
P & R Electrical (London) Ltd.
Rock Electrical Accessories Ltd.
Santon Ltd.
George H. Scholes & Co Ltd.
Superswitch Electrical Appliances Ltd.
Thermair Electrical Appliances Ltd.
Thorn Lighting Ltd.

Contents

Introduction

Home electrical work whether it is mending a fuse, fitting a plug, adding a light or socket outlet or even completely rewiring a house is within the capabilities of the keen mechanically minded d.i.y man (or woman).

Electricity, because it flows along wires instead of through pipes, cannot be seen or heard nor produces any smell, is often regarded with great mystery. This is really a fallacy since the actual wiring, fixing accessories and other associated work is very much a practical and down to earth exercise requiring no physics degree nor a college diploma. Most of the work is non-electrical and consists of lifting floorboards, drilling holes and fixing cables and boxes.

Since an electrician is paid the same rate for the job, whether he is lifting floorboards or connecting up a consumer unit, you can save a lot of money by doing the work yourself, your only outlay being materials. Prices charged by contractors vary considerably but you can take it that in general the cost of materials represent only a fraction of the total.

Safety is an important aspect. Before you start any electrical work on the house, switch off at the mains. If repairing an appliance, pull out the plug. Follow the instructions given in this book implicitly, using the correct materials and the correct sizes and types of cables and you are unlikely to go wrong.

Chapter 1
Your electrical installation

The home electrical installation is in two parts. One part belongs to the electricity board. The other part which is termed 'the consumer's installation' belongs to the house owner.

The components of the electricity board's installation consist of the incoming cable known as 'the service cable' which runs in from the street, usually underground but overhead in rural areas; the mains box con-

taining the service fuse and a neutral link; the meter, and a time switch for off-peak heating. This apparatus is connected together by cables and is sealed to prevent unauthorised persons tampering with the supply.

The householder is not concerned with the board's apparatus unless the service fuse blows and the board has to be called in to replace it. The consumer can however be held responsible for any damage to the board's equipment.

All apparatus on the house side of the meter is the responsibility of the consumer. This consists of a consumer unit or, in older houses which may not have been rewired, a number of main switch and fuse units and fuseboards.

Mains layout and equipment showing how the consumer unit is connected to the mains via the electricity meter; the earthing connections are also shown

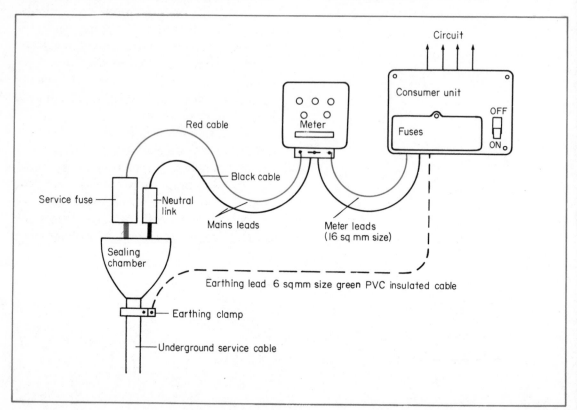

3

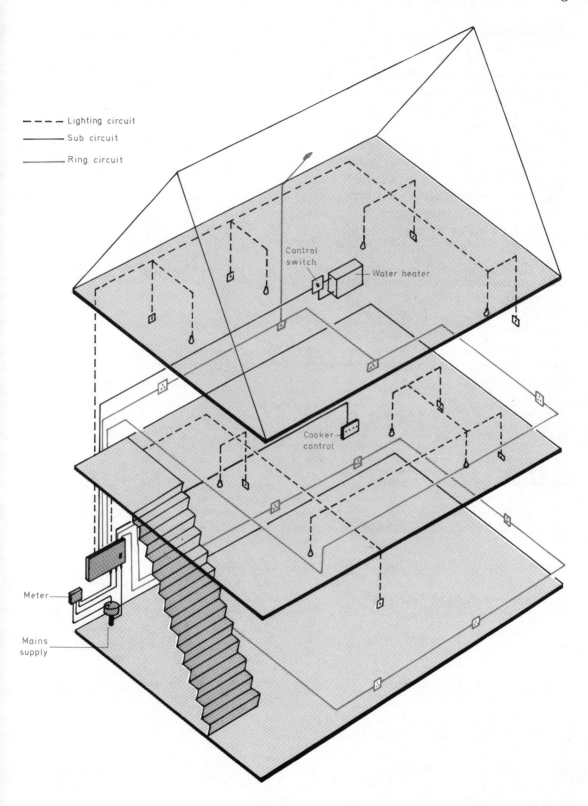

- - - - Lighting circuit
——— Sub circuit
——— Ring circuit

Control
switch

Water heater

Cooker
control

Meter

Mains
supply

4

Earthing

As will be mentioned in later sections an installation and most of the appliances have to be connected to earth. Earthing is the responsibility of the consumer and not the electricity board.

Nevertheless, the electricity board, where possible, provides earthing facilities by means of an earthing terminal situated near the meter and connected by the board to its system. This earthing is usually the metal sheathing of the underground service cable. Where the electricity board is unable to provide earthing facilities the consumer must do so. Almost invariably this will necessitate fitting an earth leakage circuit breaker to be used in conjunction with some form of earth electrode, such as an earth rod driven into the ground outside the house.

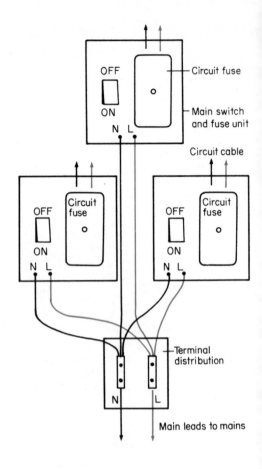

Three separate main switch and fuse units connected to the mains via a terminal distribution box, and used instead of a single consumer unit; are shown on the right

Two consumer units are shown below. One is for general use, the other for night storage heating connected to a dual-rate (white) meter

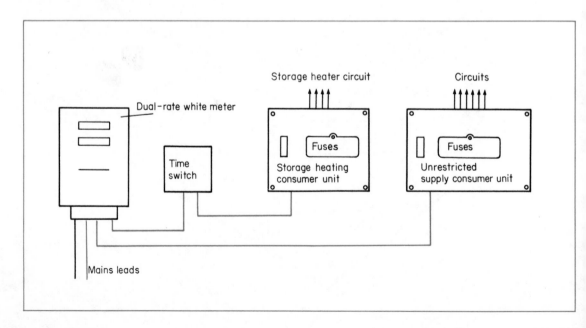

Earthing to a water pipe

Many installations are earthed to the mains water pipe by means of an earth clamp secured to the pipe on the street side of the house stop cock. Nowadays water authorities are using plastic mains pipes which means the water pipe may no longer be used as the sole means of earthing. If in doubt, it is essential to check with the electricity board whether it is advisable to use the existing water pipe earthing arrangement. When an existing water pipe can no longer be used, the electricity board requires the provision of alternative facilities which invariably means the installation of an earth leakage circuit breaker (ELCB).

Crossbonding of services

Another recent requirement is that the mains water and the mains gas services must be crossbonded to earth. This is also the responsibility of the consumer when installing new wiring or rewiring an existing installation.

To crossbond, an earthing clamp is secured to the mains water pipe on the street side of the house stop cock and to a clamp secured to the main gas pipe on the house side of the gas meter. The two clamps are connected to the installation earthing system by 6 mm² green PVC insulated cable. *(Note. At a date not later than 31 December 1977, the colour of the earth conductors and leads run independently and that of PVC sleeving to enclose the ends of bare earth conductors will be green/yellow instead of green).*

How an earth leakage circuit breaker (ELCB) operates

An ELCB is a form of main switch (actually a circuit breaker) having a tripping coil which, when energised by an earth-fault current flowing through the system, trips, opens the circuit breaker, and cuts off the power supply to the faulty circuit. It can be regarded as a main switch having an automatic switching off device. (See also Miniature Circuit Breakers).

There are two principal types of ELCB; one current operated and one voltage operated. The choice of type depends on the soil conditions and other factors. These are known to the electricity board whose advice should be sought.

The current-operated ELCB

The operation of the current-operated ELCB depends on detecting out-of-balance current in the two poles caused by the flow of earth-fault current which energises the tripping mechanism. This method has certain advantages in that it is unaffected by other ELCB's or earthing arrangements but as it requires either 1 A or ½ A to operate it. It cannot be used where the soil resistance around the earth rod is more than normal. From the illustration on page 6 you can see that neither the installation earth conductor nor the earthing lead running to the earth rod is connected to this type of ELCB.

The voltage-operated ELCB

This is a simple unit where the fault current from the installation flows directly through the tripping coil to operate the tripping mechanism. Only a small current is needed to operate it but unlike the current operated type it can be influenced by auxiliary and even spurious earthing arrangements. For example, it has been known for a fault in one house to operate the voltage earth leakage circuit breaker in another.

Two or more voltage-operated ELCBs should not be used in one installation unless the installation metal-work associated with one ELCB can be isolated from that associated with the other ELCB (or ELCBs).

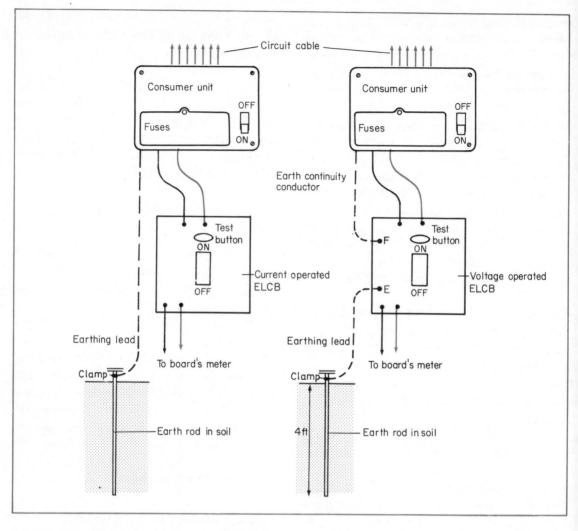

The connections at the mains for a current operated earth leakage circuit breaker and a voltage-operated earth leakage circuit breaker

The earth electrodes (earth rods) must be separated and be preferably at least 2.4 m (8ft) from other earth metal-work.

The high sensitivity ELCB

A high sensitivity ELCB is a current-operated type which operates in a fraction of a second when only a tiny current (under 30 mA) flows through the tripping coil system. This will prevent a person who comes into contact with a live wire from being electrocuted because the amount of current and the time taken for the ELCB to operate, is less than that usually required to electrocute a person.

Due to their extreme sensitivity this type of ELCB is subject to 'nuisance' tripping and is not suitable for *controlling* the whole installation, though some versions are suitable for *protecting* the complete installation. The more sensitive types which provide personal protection are used in circuits supplying power tools and similar hand-operated appliances where there is a high shock risk. Portable versions for plugging into individual socket outlets are available for use with power tools etc.

In order to be effective, the installation system has to be sound and connected to an effective means of earthing, such as an earth clamp or an earth rod.

Lighting circuits

The principal circuits of the home installation are the lighting and the power circuits.

Lighting circuits are confined principally to supplying the lighting but are sometimes used for supplying electric clock points, electric shaver sockets and small (2 A) sockets used for small appliances as well as for table lamps and floor standards.

In the two-storey house it is usual to have two lighting circuits one for each floor. In a bungalow the two circuits are, or should be, fairly evenly divided between the lighting points. In major rooms in a bungalow, the circuits could to advantage overlap so that the lighting in such rooms is supplied from more than one circuit.

Wall spot lighting

Where wall lighting and/or spot lighting is installed this can be supplied from a separate circuit. This has the advantage that the current can function when necessary as auxiliary lighting, if the fuse 'blows' in the main lighting circuit.

Power circuits

Power circuits are usually defined as circuits supplying socket outlets used for portable heaters and other appliances. The term, though not strictly accurate, stems from the days when electricity authorities charged a high rate for lighting and a lower rate for power (power meaning 15 A socket outlets), with special (low) rates for cooking and water heating.

Ring and radial circuits

Modern power circuits are chiefly wired in the form of a ring and as such are called ring circuits. Other power circuits are termed radial power circuits which supply two, or in some circumstances a maximum of six, 13 A socket outlets (power points) from the one circuit.

A ring circuit is limited to supplying socket outlets and fixed appliances over an area of 100 m² (1080 ft²). Where a floor area exceeds this, two (or more) ring circuits are necessary. For the average two-storey house even having a total floor area under 100 m², it is usual and desirable to install two ring circuits one for each floor.

Radial power circuits are installed in situations where a number of socket outlets are required but it is not worth installing a ring circuit.

Other house circuits

Other circuits which may be installed in the home include; cooker circuits, water heater circuits, outside circuits (e.g. garage), and storage heating circuits.

Current rating of circuits

Each circuit is given a specific current rating. This current rating determines the size of cable in which the circuit is wired, the maximum load (watts) which a circuit can carry at any one time, and the current rating (size) of fuse that is to protect that circuit. It is a requirement of the regulations that the current rating of a circuit fuse must not be greater than the current rating of the smallest conductor (wire or cable) in that circuit. Current ratings of circuits in the home which range from 5A for lighting to 45 A for large cookers are given in Table 1a at the end of this chapter.

Circuit cables

It has already been explained that sizes of cables vary with the particular circuit. These circuit cables are those used for the fixed wiring and should not be confused with flexible cords. The latter are used to connect lights to fixed wiring via ceiling roses, electrical appliances to fixed wiring via socket outlets, fused connection units or other outlet points. In most houses and bungalows the type of cable used for fixed wiring is 2-core and earth PVC sheathed. Blocks of flats and some houses are wired in insulated cable run in metal or plastic conduit. This is a professional job outside the scope of the d.i.y. man, but the cable sizes are the same as with PVC sheathed.

It will be seen from Table 1b that fixed wiring cable sizes range from 1.0 mm² used for a lighting circuit to 10 mm² used in some cooker circuits. When you have a wiring job to do, whether an extension or a complete circuit, you must select the appropriate cable size.

Metric and Imperial sizes

Cables in Britain have been made in metric sizes for some years and have replaced imperial sizes entirely. However, as most installations were wired with imperial size cables it is necessary to know the equivalents, especially when extending a circuit. These are shown in Table 1a.

Circuit fuses

Every circuit must be protected by a fuse or similar device which will operate on excessive overload, short circuits and—where earthing conditions are good—on line-to-earth faults. Where earthing conditions are not good, ELCBs must be used.

Fuses are made in four principal current

ratings—5, 15, 20, and 30 A. A fifth size, having a 45 A current rating, has been recently introduced. Table 2 gives the current rating of fuses for circuits and 13 A plugs. The fuses are usually arranged in a consumer unit or a fuseboard but can be in individual switch fuse units.

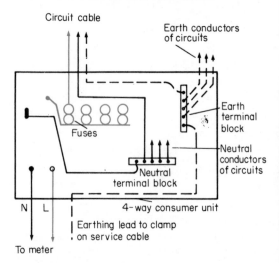

The internal connections of a typical 4-way consumer unit with one circuit connected to the fuseway, the other three circuits still to be wired

Consumer units (and modern fuseboards) are designed to allow fuse units of any of the four current ratings (5-30 A) to be inserted in any of the fuseways and in any order. A consumer unit will therefore have fuses of mixed ratings according to the circuits supplied, but preferably ranged in the order of the fuse of highest current rating to be adjacent to the main switch and the lowest rated fuse at the extreme end.

Where a consumer unit has spare fuseways and the function and current ratings of future circuits are not known, it is usual to blank these off using blanking plates supplied.

Types of fuse

There are two types of fuses: rewirable and cartridge. The majority of fuses installed in dwellings are of the rewirable type. The cartridge fuse is superior to the rewirable, but must be replaced by a new cartridge; it cannot be mended.

The fuse unit comprises a fuse holder, a fuse element, and a base or shield. The fuse holder is either of plastic or ceramic, and has two knife contacts one at each end for inserting into corresponding contacts in the consumer unit.

The fuse element of the rewirable fuse is tinned copper fuse wire which is secured in the fuse holder by terminal screws. The fuse element of cartridge fuses is totally enclosed in the cartridge and cannot be rewired. The cartridge is secured in its holder by spring contacts or is a close-fit in a tubular contact.

Fuse holders and fuse shields, where fitted, are colour coded according to their current rating as in Table 2. The knife contacts of fuse holders are usually of different physical dimensions according to their current rating so that a fuse of a given rating, say 30 A, is not inserted in one of lower current rating. Cartridges are also of different physical dimensions making it impossible to load say a 5 A fuse holder with a 15 A, 20 A or 30 A cartridge.

Although rewirable fuse holders are of different dimensions according to their current rating it is possible to rewire a fuse with heavier fuse wire than the fuse rating. This is undesirable as it creates a potentially dangerous situation.

Miniature circuit breakers (MCBs)

The miniature circuit breaker is fitted into some consumer units in place of fuses. It is a single-pole automatic switch which trips when the circuit is being subjected to serious overload or a fault occurs in the circuit.

The MCBs are available in similar current ratings to circuit fuses, and, where intended to be used in the same consumer's units, carry the same colour markings. The MCB is superior to a fuse, is more reliable and acts with greater speed and with a smaller overload current. Although the initial cost is more than that of a fuse, once fitted MCBs save the trouble and cost of renewing fuses.

An MCB cannot be closed (switched on) against a fault and cannot be abused, as can be done with a fuse by fitting a larger diameter of fuse wire. Another advantage is that individual circuits can be switched off or left on as required. For example, a circuit supplying a refrigerator or freezer can be left on when all other circuits are switched off because the house is being left unoccupied for a period, e.g. holidays.

Cable colours

The 2-core and earth PVC sheathed cable used in home wiring has two insulated cores (wires) and one uninsulated wire. One insulated wire is coloured black, the other red. The red wire is always used in the live pole. The black is used in the neutral pole of a circuit but is sometimes used in the live pole. For example, the 2-core and earth cables running to a switch are used for the live and the switch return wire respectively which means that one is black; this is usually the switch return wire. To avoid confusion the ends of the switch return wire should be enclosed in red PVC sleeving though this is not always done.

The uninsulated wire running through a cable between the two insulated wires is the earth continuity conductor (ecc). Where the sheath of the cable is removed, i.e. at a switch, ceiling rose, socket outlet, joint box, consumer unit or any other termination, the end of the wire is enclosed in green PVC sleeving.

In some sections of a lighting circuit, 3-core and earth PVC sheathed cable is used. This is in 2-way switching circuits

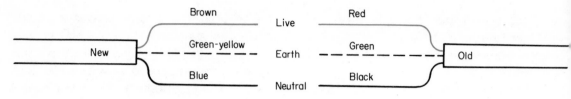

When connecting 'old' and 'new' 3-core flex the cable colours must be connected as shown. The same applies when replacing old flex with new flex

and where two lights are controlled by a 2-gang switch, with a 3-core and earth cable running from a joint box to the switch unit.

The 3-core and earth cable has three insulated wires and an uninsulated earth wire. The core colours are red, yellow, and blue. These colours have no significance in domestic wiring, as the cable is made for 3-phase power circuits in non-domestic installations. The colours are useful for identification but the ends should be enclosed at switch circuits in red PVC sleeving.

Eventually the colours of the cores of fixed wiring cables will be changed as they have been for flexible cords. The colours are under discussion by the various authorities representing the electrical installation industry but have not yet been finalised. This is because each country has its own national colour coding for cables so it must not be assumed that the colours adopted will be the same as for flexible cords. The new colours are expected to be introduced in the 1980's.

Table 1a HOUSE WIRING CABLES (PVC sheathed)

Metric Size of conductor mm²	Imperial size (old) No. and diam. of wires	Current rating (nominal)* (A)
1.0	1/.044	12
1.5	3/.029	15
2.5	7/.029	21
4	7/.036	27
6	7/.044	35
10	7/.064	48
16	19/.044	64

*These ratings are for circuits protected by rewirable fuses
For cartridge fuses and MCBs a one-third higher current rating is applied

Table 1b CIRCUIT CABLES AND FUSES

Circuit	Cable used (mm²)	Circuit fuse (A)
Lighting	1.0 or 1.5	5
Immersion heater or other 15 A circuits	1.5	15
Immersion heater (alternative) storage heaters and 20 A radial circuits and instantaneous water heaters to 5 kW rating	2.5	20
Ring circuit and spurs	2.5	30
Small family size cookers Instantaneous water heaters to 7 kW Radial circuits (30 A)	4.0	30*
Large size cookers	6.0	45
Meter tails from consumer unit	10 or 16	Service fuse (electricity board)

*Cartridge fuse or MCB; otherwise use 6 mm² cable

Table 2 CAPACITY OF FUSES

Current rating (A)	Colour	Fuse wire size, diam. (mm)	Current rating (A)	Colour
CIRCUIT FUSES			13 A PLUG FUSES	
5	White	0.20	13	Brown
15	Blue	0.50	3	Red (or blue)
20	Yellow	0.60	10	Black*
30	Red	0.85	5	Black*
45	Green	1.25	2	Black*

*These fuses are used for special purposes

Chapter 2
Rewiring

The rewiring of a house may become necessary for a variety of reasons, i.e.

(i) The cables are old and their insulation is perished.

(ii) Equipment and accessories are out of date and lights, switches and socket outlets are needed in new positions.

(iii) The original wiring has been extended indiscriminately with too many lights on one circuit and various types and sizes of cable have been used. This type of installation can be generally regarded as unsatisfactory and possibly potentially dangerous.

Rewiring usually means replacing all cables and most wiring accessories such as ceiling roses, switches and socket outlets. It may not be necessary to rewire all the circuits but, where there are any doubts, it is as well to make a 'clean sweep' and rewire the whole installation.

Which circuits need rewiring?

The lighting circuit is the principal circuit which is likely to need rewiring for it is usually the oldest circuit in the house. The older type of power circuit, which is described elsewhere, will also need rewiring.

Circuits which will not require rewiring are as follows.

Ring circuits

If a ring circuit has been installed during the last 20 years and the cables are PVC sheathed (or PVC insulated if an all-conduit installation) or in MICC (mineral insulated copper covered) cable, they should not need rewiring. The opportunity should be taken, however, to bring the circuits up to date and to add more socket outlets.

Cooker circuit

A cooker circuit should not need rewiring unless the cable is very old and is not PVC sheathed (or PVC insulated if run in conduit). The cable used for a cooker circuit is of comparatively large size and expensive so there is no point in rewiring the circuit unless essential.

Water heater circuits

If an immersion heater circuit, or a circuit for a shower unit, or for any other electric water heater has been installed in recent years, it should not need rewiring.

Lighting circuit extensions

Where a lighting circuit has been extended using new cables and modern wiring accessories the new sections should not need rewiring with the main lighting circuits. These extensions can form part of the new wiring.

Outdoor electrical extensions

A cable running to a detached garage, greenhouse or shed, if installed correctly and using proper cable to conform with the IEE Wiring Regulations need not be disturbed. Otherwise it should be disconnected from the mains until it has either been rewired or modified to bring it into line with the regulations.

Under no circumstances may a detached garage or other outside building be supplied from a flexible cord connected to a socket outlet or other outlet in the house.

Inspecting an installation for rewiring

It is usually obvious when a house needs rewiring but as the installation will probably continue to give good service it is as well to conduct a methodical inspection and where possible to carry out tests.

Tests using instruments

Instruments are available for testing an installation and are used by electrical contractors and electricity boards. These test the insulation of cables, the continuity of the earthing and whether the earthing system is effective under fault conditions.

All-insulated wiring systems

An all-insulated wiring system, wired in TRS (tough rubber sheathed) cable or PVC sheathed cable, will usually show good results from an insulation test. This is the case even though the wiring may be in a poor state and the insulation perished, but dry. If part of the wiring, especially where the cable is jointed at switches and ceiling roses, is damp the test result will be poor, even if the remainder of the wiring is in good condition. Also an insulation test may not give an accurate result. This applies particularly to a lighting circuit having no earth conductor.

'Breaks' in metal conduit are quite common in houses and destroy the continuity of the earthing system. Most likely spots where 'breaks' occur are shown

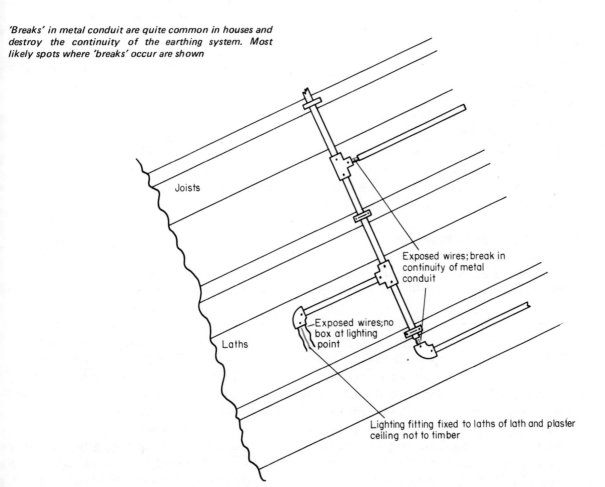

Joists

Exposed wires; break in continuity of metal conduit

Exposed wires; no box at lighting point

Laths

Lighting fitting fixed to laths of lath and plaster ceiling not to timber

Metal sheathed systems

If an installation, or parts of it, are wired in lead sheathed cable (as are many older installations), or it is an all-metal conduit installation with the lead sheath or metal conduit earthed, an insulation test will usually give an accurate result. Insulation tests can be inconclusive, if not misleading, and a physical examination of the wiring is essential to ascertain whether a rewire is required.

Tests using proper instruments will be carried out by the electricity board on request. This service is often free of charge and the board will also present a report on the installation. A similar service is also provided by registered electrical contractors.

Examining wiring and accessories

The first preliminary to rewiring is to make a thorough examination of the wires and accessories, in the loft, under the floorboards, in the meter cupboard and wherever there are cables and wiring accessories.

An inspection in the roof space or loft gives a good indication of the general quality and condition of the wiring throughout the house. If it is a conduit installation, check that the conduit is secured to joists and other fixings by saddles or clips. The conduit should be continuous and secured in the Tees, elbows, conduit boxes and other conduit fittings.

Where a metal conduit has come adrift from a conduit fitting, the earth continuity of the conduit is broken. If the conduit is the earth continuity conductor the earthing of the circuit will also be broken. The wires may also be exposed at these breaks and create a potentially dangerous situation. Also check whether any lengths of conduit have been damaged; one of the most likely places is in the vicinity of the cold water

storage tank. Damage can often be caused here after the ball valve mechanism in the tank has been repaired.

Check whether any wires are exposed at the ends of conduit terminating at lighting points. The conduit should terminate in a conduit box but these boxes are often omitted leaving the wires exposed.

Inspecting sheathed cable installations

In the roof space one can usually tell at a glance whether the cables are neatly run over and between joists and securely clipped in position. All too often they are loose and have become tangled over the years. If there are joint boxes, check that these are secured to timber supports and that no unsheathed ends of the cables are outside joint boxes.

If lead-sheathed cable is used, the sheath must be electrically continuous and earthed. If the sheath has become detached from the metal clamping plate of a lead-sheathed cable joint box the earth continuity will be broken.

Cables at switch drops

Sheathed cables dropping down the walls to switches are usually enclosed in conduit, the top end of the conduit terminating correctly below the tops of joists. Check whether the conduit is damaged, and whether it has a rubber bush on the end to protect the cable sheath. If there is no rubber bush or it is damaged, check whether the cable sheath is also damaged. A second bush should be fitted at the lower end of the conduit but this can be checked only when the switch is removed.

The switch drop conduit of conduit installations is part of the earth continuity system and should be secured to the main conduit at an elbow or Tee fitting.

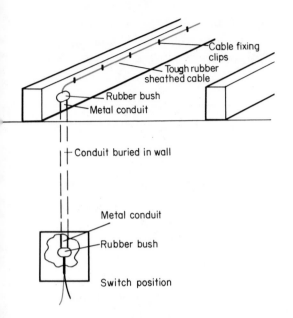

Sheathed cables in the loft or roof space are clipped to the sides of joists and PVC (or rubber) bushes are placed on the ends of metal conduits at switch drops

Cables under floorboards

A similar inspection should be made of cables under the floorboards. These are less likely to have been damaged than those in the roof space, unless the floorboards have been lifted for installing central heating or for any other major alterations.

However, since the cables are out of sight once the floorboards are relaid, this wiring is often subject to bad workmanship, especially when extensions are made to an original installation. Special attention should be paid to joint boxes. Check also whether too many cables have been inserted in the joint boxes preventing the covers being screwed on properly.

It is not practicable to check more than a portion of cables under the floorboards. If you lift one or two boards which have obviously been raised before, a good indication of the state of the wiring can be gained.

Inspection at switch and light positions

It is here that cables usually show the first signs of deterioration and whether the insulation has perished. The same goes for the cables at socket-outlets of power circuits.

The principal reasons for deterioration are:

(i)   Excess temperatures occur because of poor contacts at switches; heat transfer from the lamps of close ceiling fittings and batten lamp-holders; overloading and/or poor contact between a plug and its socket.

(ii) Insulation may have been damaged when replacing or changing switches, lighting fittings and socket-outlets, especially when the insulation is already perished.

To check the cable at a switch, first turn off the electricity at the mains, and remove the switch. Carefully examine the insulation of the wires and note whether it is brittle or perished. Repeat the process at a number of switch points.

Where the switch is the old round, tumbler action type mounted on a hardwood block it is as well to remove the block as well as the switch. Then the cables, if they are buried, can be examined right up to the point where they come out of the wall, and up to the conduit or sheath if they are fixed to the wall surface.

If the switches are the modern 'square' rocker or doily action type they will be mounted on either plastic surface boxes or in metal boxes sunk into the wall. The sheath of a sheathed cable should extend into the box (or the conduit fixed to the box) allowing the wires to be properly examined. If the boxes (and switches) have been fitted in recent years to modernise the installation it may be necessary to remove the box in order to examine the insulation at the end of the sheathing.

The insulation on old TRS cables will almost certainly have hardened or perished and will pull off the conductor. These cables must be replaced by rewiring.

Replacing switches

When a switch has been removed to examine the cables and, in so doing the insulation has come off leaving the conductor bare and uninsulated, the switch can be replaced temporarily until rewiring. However, it is necessary to enclose the bare wires in PVC sleeving and wrap PVC adhesive insulation tape over the sleeving to ensure that it is properly electrically insulated.

Inspecting wiring to lighting points

To inspect the ends of cables at lighting fittings it is usually necessary to remove the ceiling rose or ceiling fitting plate. The insulation of the wires is examined as for the switches and, where necessary, the insulation should be fortified with PVC sleeving and PVC insulation tape.

Where a ceiling rose or a lighting fitting has more than two terminals and therefore more than two bunches of wires take care not to separate jointed wires otherwise you will have difficulty in identifying wires to restore the current throughout the circuit or to get the light to operate normally.

Inspection at socket-outlets

Having turned off the power supplying these circuits, select the socket-outlets which can be removed for inspection of the cables. If the socket-outlets are known to be wired on the old radial system the cir-

cuits will have to be rewired so there will be no advantage in removing the sockets to examine the condition of the cables.

If wired on the ring circuit system, you

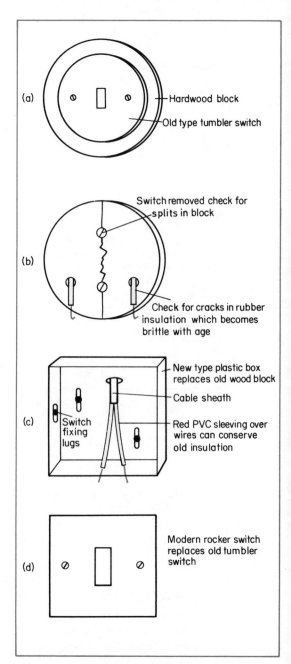

Replacing an obsolete tumbler switch with a modern plate switch. (a) and (b) show the existing switch and blocks, (c) is the new switch mounting box and (d) plate-switch connected and fixed

Labels in figure:

(a) Hardwood block / Old type tumbler switch

(b) Switch removed check for splits in block / Check for cracks in rubber insulation which becomes brittle with age

(c) New type plastic box replaces old wood block / Cable sheath / Red PVC sleeving over wires can conserve old insulation / Switch fixing lugs

(d) Modern rocker switch replaces old tumbler switch

can check whether TRS cable or PVC cable has been used. If the wiring is TRS the cables should be replaced as the insulation is likely to be perished.

The fact that the socket-outlets are the modern 13 A type with flat pin fused plugs does not mean that a ring circuit is used or that the cables are fairly new. The sockets may have replaced the old roundpin type and connected to the old wiring. If they are replacements, it is as well to check that the circuit contains an earth conductor and is connected to the earth terminals of the sockets.

When checking sockets it is better to select those fixed to the skirting or to a wood surface to save replugging the wall to refix sockets or the mounting boxes.

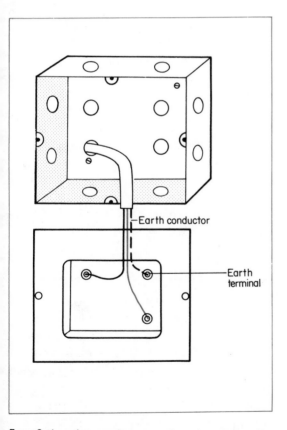

Every 3-pin socket must have an earth conductor connected to the earth terminal of the socket. The earth conductor is within the sheathed cable

Inspecting consumer units

An installation having a number of main switch and fuse units instead of one composite unit supplying all circuits is a good indication that it is old and in need of an early rewire.

If you inherit such an installation it will be as well to examine the switchgear for cracked or broken covers and also that the main switches actually work and switch off when the handle is operated. Also open the switch covers — these are or should be interlocked with the operating handles so that the switch is turned off before the cover can be opened.

Having opened the cover of a main switch and fuse unit, check the fuseholders. Check whether the porcelain is broken exposing the live contacts and the fuse wires are of the current rating given in Table 2 on page 11. It is also important to check whether the fuse wire is of the correct current rating for the circuit. Also check whether single- or double-pole fusing. Double-pole fusing should not now be used. The fuseholder in the neutral pole should contain a larger wire than the size of fuse wire in the live pole. It should be a wire, and not a fuse wire.

Earthing too is important. Old switch units usually have a metal casing which must be earthed by means of an earth conductor connected to an earth terminal on the outside of the casing. The earth conductor is almost certain to be uninsulated since an insulated earth cable only became essential about a decade ago. If the uninsulated earth cable is green with corrosion it must be renewed prior to rewiring if the installation is connected to the electricity supply and therefore in current use.

The modern consumer unit was not introduced into domestic installations until the late 1940's but since then it has been fitted to a number of old installations without those installations being rewired.

The existence of a modern consumer unit does not necessarily mean that the circuit cables are in a good condition.

Checking a modernised installation

Where a new consumer unit has been fitted to an old installation to replace obsolete switchgear, there are usually obvious signs of this.

An examination of the cables may show that some are TRS or VRI in conduit, or lead-sheathed. Some cables will probably be PVC sheathed running into, and connected to, the new consumer unit. These may be entirely new circuits, such as ring circuits, but some may be a new final length of cable which has replaced a length of old cable too short to be connected to the new consumer unit. Do not therefore be surprised to find old cables at the switches and lighting fittings, and in the roof space and under the floorboards, with new cables at the consumer unit. These new lengths of cables may be used as the first sections of circuits when rewiring.

Checking an old earthing system

An old installation due for rewiring is unlikely to have effective earthing throughout, apart from the lighting circuits which were normally not earthed. Also, it is most likely that the installation will be earthed to the mains water pipe, whereas nowadays the mains water pipe may no longer be used as the sole means of earthing. This is because the water authorities are using plastic pipes in their mains systems. The effectiveness of the earthing will be checked when conducting the earth continuity tests and earth loop impedance tests.

Deciding on rewiring

When you have decided that a rewire is necessary you will have to make the following decisions:

1. Time of year to do the work.
2. Whether the whole installation should be rewired at the one time.
3. Whether all the existing wiring needs to be rewired.
4. If 'YES' to (2), which sections and which circuits will be wired first.
5. Whether, and for how long, you can manage without electricity. It is an advantage to rewire during the summer with its long days and little need for electric heating.
6. Whether you can have a temporary supply of electricity, if only for lighting in the roof space.

The time of year is a personal choice, bearing in mind the advantages of doing the work during the lighter days.

It is not essential to wire all the circuits or sections at one time, nor is it necessary to pull out all the old wiring before starting on the new. Old wiring is usually best pulled out as the rewiring progresses.

If more convenient, you may rewire one circuit at a time, for example, the upstairs lighting circuit in the spring. This will leave another lighting circuit until, say, the autumn.

Programme for rewiring

You can start rewiring at any point, but, in a 2-storey house, it is usually best to rewire the upper floor first. Most of the wiring is in the roof space and by tackling this circuit first you can have portable lighting plugged into socket outlets of the ring circuit, or other circuit if you have yet to instal ring circuits.

Next, rewire the ground floor lighting as most of these cables are laid under the floorboards of the first floor rooms. To raise the necessary floorboards you will have to shift heavy furniture and lift floor coverings which may include linoleum and wall-to-wall fitted carpets.

You will not want to move furniture and lift floor coverings more than once. Any other circuits to be rewired, or new circuits to be installed, should be done at the same time where the cables run under the floorboards of the same rooms. These other circuits are likely to be the ring circuit supplying socket-outlets and fixed appliances in the first floor rooms, landing and other service areas; circuits supplying immersion heaters and/or water heaters; and the cooker circuit in cases where this cable cannot be laid under the ground floor because the floor is solid or has a floor covering such as adhesive tiles preventing access to floorboards.

The last circuit to rewire or to instal as an entirely new circuit is the ring circuit feeding socket-outlets in the ground floor rooms. The cables of this circuit are run under the floor. If the floor is solid, then the cable may be run behind the skirting or, where this is not practicable, you will have to run the cable under the floorboards of the upstairs rooms and down the walls to the socket-outlets in the rooms below.

Availability of electricity

Plan the work so that you have mains electricity available until the very last stages of the job. It is not necessary to remove the old main switch and fuse units until you are ready to fix the new consumer unit.

To rewire a circuit, remove the cable from the fuse unit and when the rewired circuit is completed and all accessories connected and fixed, connect it temporarily to the old switch and fuse unit. Then, when all circuits are rewired arrangements can be made for the electricity board to disconnect the supply temporarily. They will do this by withdrawing the service fuse and disconnecting the cables from the meter.

The old switchgear can then be removed and the new consumer unit fixed. Connect the circuit cables to the consumer unit and arrange with the Board to have the supply reconnected. This last job should not take more than a few hours so if you arrange for the Board to disconnect the supply early one morning and reconnect it later the same day you need not be without electricity overnight.

A typical consumer unit suitable for use when re-wiring. The cover is removed showing connections of the circuit cable and mains cables. The fuse units (or mcbs) are yet to be fitted

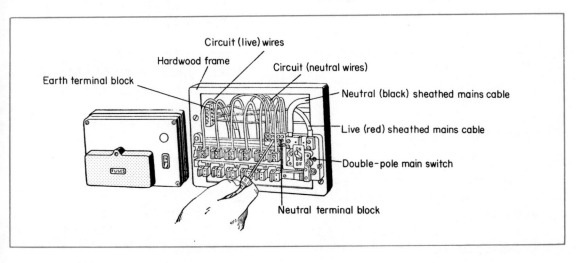

Although the job will normally take only a few hours to complete, snags sometimes arise and you may not finish in one day. When this is likely allow more time for the work.

Alternatively, you can sometimes fix the consumer unit at the start of the job and have the unit connected to the mains at the same time as the old units are disconnected. You can then temporarily connect them to the new consumer unit yourself. When the rewiring is completed you request the Board to come and test the installation and connect it permanently to the mains. This is requested by completing a consumer's application form.

Utilising an existing consumer unit

Where a modern consumer unit is already installed you have no need to contact the electricity board until the rewiring is completed. The rewired circuits can be connected to the appropriate fuseways, having earlier disconnected the old circuit wires.

Permission to rewire

If you own the house, bungalow or flat you do not have to seek permission from any person or organisation to rewire it or to carry out any electrical work on the consumer side of the installation. However, if you are a tenant you must inform the landlord of your intentions. In either case you do not have to ask the electricity board or the local council for permission to rewire.

Tips on rewiring

The procedure and method of rewiring adopted depends upon many factors and the following tips apply to most, if not all, circumstances.

1. Decide on the positions of each light, switch, socket outlet and other points including fixed appliances.
2. Determine the circuits and draw up a schedule (see Table 3).
3. Where the positions of lighting points are to be different from those they are to replace, mark the new positions on walls and ceilings etc.
4. Decide on the routes for the cable runs and which existing runs can be utilised to save cutting away more woodwork and brickwork in the house structure.
5. So far as possible make use of existing conduits dropping down to switches.
6. When existing metal conduits are used, fit a PVC or rubber bush at each end of the conduit.
7. Cable and conduit buried in walls and fixed in inaccessable places can be abandoned but seal the ends of cables where there is a possibility during rewiring that the conductors are live when switching on the power.
8. Where there is no existing buried conduit at a switch drop for enclosing the cable and the wall is not being repapered, fix the cables to the surface of the wall and sink them later when redecorating.
9. When you bury sheathed PVC cable in walls no conduit or other protection against mechanical damage is normally required.
10. When raising floorboards look out for boards which have been previously raised. When raising T and G (tongued and grooved) floorboards which have not been raised before you may need a rip saw to remove the tongues. Before raising boards take care not to cut cables and pipes which are beneath them.
11. Cables crossing joists under floorboards have to be threaded through holes drilled in the joists at least 50 mm (2 in) from the tops.

Electric bells, buzzers and chimes

These operate at elv (extra low voltages) between 3 and 12 V. The single bell, buzzer and many models of chimes are powered by dry batteries but the more powerful chimes and intricate bell systems have to operate from mains transformers. Usually a transformer is preferable for any bell or chimes. Where an illuminated bell push is used a mains transformer is essential as the lamp of the push would exhaust a battery in a day or so.

The purpose-made bell transformer is double wound and the secondary winding is connected to earth so that should a fault occur in the transformer, the low voltage apparatus and wiring would not be subjected to mains voltage. The transformer is supplied from a 5 A circuit or from a fused connection unit (with 3 A fuse) served by the ring circuit, using 1.0 mm² 2-core and earth PVC sheathed cable.

This cable is connected to the 240 V mains or primary terminals of the transformer and the elv bell wire is connected to two of the three elv output or secondary terminals of the transformer. The three terminals give a choice of 3, 5, and 8 V with most transformers. Some chimes require a higher voltage and for these, mains transformers are available with terminals giving 4, 8 and 12 V.

Burglar alarms

These are bought in kit form for connection to a battery. For this purpose batteries are more reliable than the mains supply and remain permanently in operation, provided the batteries are replaced when necessary.

Materials required for rewiring

Draw up a list of materials needed. For a 3-bedroom house (wired as the schedule in Table 3) the following materials would be needed.

Table 3 TYPICAL SCHEDULE OF POINTS FOR REWIRING

Location	Lights	Switches	Socket outlets	Other outlets
Living room	1 pendant 3 wall lights	1 rocker 1 rocker	4 doubles 2 singles	—
Dining room	1 pendant	1 rocker	4 doubles	—
Kitchen	1 pendant	1 rocker	4 doubles	Cooker
Hall	1 pendant	1 rocker	1 single	Door chimes
Porch	1 porch fitting	1 rocker (in hall)	—	—
W.C. (outside)	1 batten lampholder	1 rocker	—	—
Bedroom No 1	2 pendants	1 rocker 1 cord operated	4 doubles	—
Bedroom No 2	1 pendant	1 rocker	3 doubles	—
Bedroom No 3	1 pendant	1 rocker	3 doubles	—
Bathroom	1 close ceiling fitting	1 cord operated	None	—
W.C.	1 batten lampholder	1 rocker	None	—
Landing	1 pendant	2 2-way (1 in hall)	{ 1 double Immersion heater in tank cupboard	
Garage	2 (1 fluorescent)	2	2 doubles	—

Lighting circuit

Up to 100 m of 1.0 mm² 2-core and earth PVC sheathed cable.
6 m (approx.) of 1.0 mm² 3-core and earth PVC sheathed cable.
10 m (approx.) green PVC insulated cable (2.5 mm²) for earthing and bonding.*
3 m (approx.) green PVC sleeving.*
One box of plastic cable fixing clips.
Three 4-terminal plastic joint boxes.
Nine loop-in ceiling roses, lampholders and flexible cord. If special pendants are to be bought, one fewer ceiling rose and lampholder will be required for each.
Two batten lampholders.
Eight one-way rocker switches.
Two 2-gang rocker switches.
One 2-way rocker switch.
Thirteen switch mounting boxes, plaster depth metal for flush mounting and slim plastic for surface mounting.
Two cord operated ceiling switches.
Three wall lights.
Three mounting boxes for wall lights complete with cable protection grommets.
Assorted screws, nails, etc.

After 31 December 1977 colour will be green/yellow as in flex.

Ring circuit

50 m (approx.) of 2.5 mm² 2-core and earth PVC sheathed cable.
One box of cable fixing clips.
Three single switched (or unswitched if preferred) 13 A socket-outlets
Three one-gang surface of flush mounting boxes.
Twenty-five double 13 A socket-outlets (switched or unswitched).
Twenty-five 2-gang surface or flush mounting boxes.
Assorted wood screws, etc.

Immersion heater circuit

One length of 2-core and earth 2.5 mm² PVC sheathed cable, sufficient to run from the consumer unit.
One 20 A double-pole water heater switch or other controls (according to the type of immersion heater and the method of control required).
1 m (approx.) 2.5 mm² 3-core heat resisting flex.
Fixing screws, cable fixing clips and other small items as needed.

Cooker circuit

One length of 6 mm² 2-core and earth PVC sheathed cable; to run from consumer unit to cooker control unit fixed near the cooker about 1.5 m above floor level. An additional length of this cable (preferably with white sheath) to run from control unit to cooker.
A quantity of cable fixing clips.
One cooker control unit, with or without 13 A kettle socket and with or without pilot lights (neon indicators).
One surface mounting box or flush box for the control unit.
One cable terminal box or cable outlet box (optional) for connecting the final cable to the cooker.

Chimes or bell circuit

One door chimes or bell (or buzzer).
One mains transformer for the chimes.
One bell push.
A quantity of bell wire and insulated staples.

Main switchgear

One 8-way consumer unit fitted with two 5 A, three 30 A, one 20 A fuses or mcbs and two blanking plates for the spare fuseways.

Chapter 3
The lighting system

The home lighting system consists mainly of lighting circuits devoted to supplying fixed lighting only. Other lighting is sometimes termed auxiliary lighting, but in some rooms this may, in fact, constitute the main lighting.

Auxiliary lighting comprises spot lights, pelmet lighting and other special lighting and effects. This lighting can often be more conveniently supplied from the ring circuit via a special fused outlet (see ring circuits, Chapter 5). Table lamps and floor standards are also supplied from a ring circuit via plugs and socket-outlets. An advantage of supplying this type of lighting from a ring circuit, apart from convenience in wiring, is that room and other area lighting is supplied from two circuits, so that in the event of a fuse blowing the room is not blacked out.

Lighting circuits

A lighting circuit consists of a number of lighting points individually controlled by switches. These are usually fixed to the wall near the access door but in some instances, such as in the bathroom, the lighting control is from a cord-operated switch fixed to the ceiling.

Some lights, especially the landing light, and the general light in a bedroom, are controlled by two switches. For the landing light, one switch is on the landing, the other in the hall. In the bedroom, the second switch is usually at the bedhead. Two-switch control of a light is known as '2-way switching' which is a special switching circuit. These circuits are dealt with later in this chapter.

A light can also be controlled by three or more switches located in different positions. This is termed 'intermediate switching' and is a development of the 2-way switching circuit by the insertion of special switches in intermediate positions. The switches are termed intermediate switches.

Maximum lights for a circuit

A lighting circuit has a current rating of 5 A which is the maximum current that the circuit may carry at any given time. As lights on a circuit are switched on and off when required and the wattage of the bulbs inserted in the lampholders of lighting fittings varies with the situation and the requirements of the household, a method of current assessment has been worked out to ensure that a lighting circuit is unlikely to be overloaded. Assessment is made on the basis of the number of lampholders. For instance, a plain pendant has one lampholder whereas a multi-light fitting has two, three or more lampholders.

Each lampholder is then assessed at 100 W where the bulb in the lampholder is no more than of 100 W rating. Where larger bulbs are fitted, the actual wattage is used in the calculation. The total effective wattage of a 5 A lighting circuit is 1200 W. This is obtained by multiplying the current rating of the circuit (5 A) by the voltage of the supply, which in the UK is 240 volts, giving:

$$240 \times 5 = 1200 \text{ W.}$$

If no lampholder has a bulb larger than 100 W a lighting circuit may have 12 lampholders.

Number of lighting points and lighting circuits

To allow for a number of multi-light fittings and perhaps a couple of 150 W bulbs, the number of lighting points to a circuit in the home should not exceed eight but preferably no more than six. The fewer lights on a circuit the less the inconvenience should a fuse blow. Also, by having only six lights on a circuit when originally wired there is greater scope for the addition of extra lighting points.

The lighting in the home should be divided fairly evenly over two circuits which for the average 2-storey house means a circuit for each floor. In a bungalow or flat the lighting can be divided over two circuits as desired with the main living rooms being supplied from both circuits where they have more than one light.

Wiring a lighting circuit

There are two principal methods of wiring a lighting circuit, the loop-in system and the joint box system. In practice a circuit is often a mixture of both methods, the principal sections being loop-in with some lighting points being wired in conjunction with joint boxes to save cable and to facilitate the wiring. For both methods twin-core and earth PVC sheathed cable is used.

The joint box method of wiring a lighting circuit showing the connections at the joint boxes and ceiling roses. Additional joint boxes are connected in the same manner

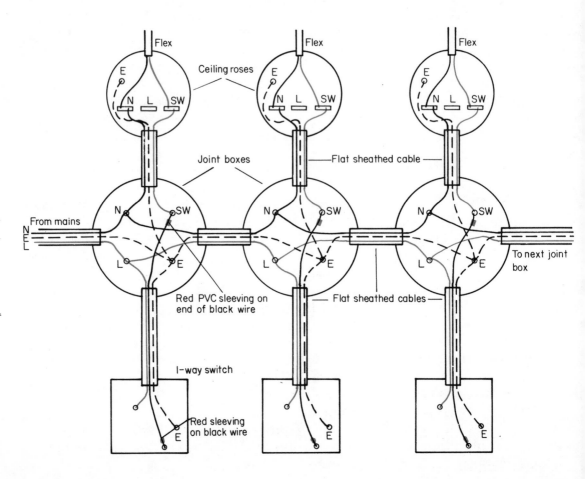

The loop-in system

In the loop-in system, ceiling roses combine the functions of ceiling rose and joint box as the circuit wires are jointed at the ceiling rose terminals. The flexible cord of the pendant is connected to the rose terminals.

When wiring the circuit, the twin and earth cable is run from the consumer unit to each of the lighting points in turn and terminates at the last. The cable is therefore looped in and out of the ceiling rose, hence its name. From each ceiling rose a length of

The loop-in method of wiring three lighting points. Additional ceiling roses are added as needed to complete the circuit. The lower diagram shows how the connections within the ceiling rose are made

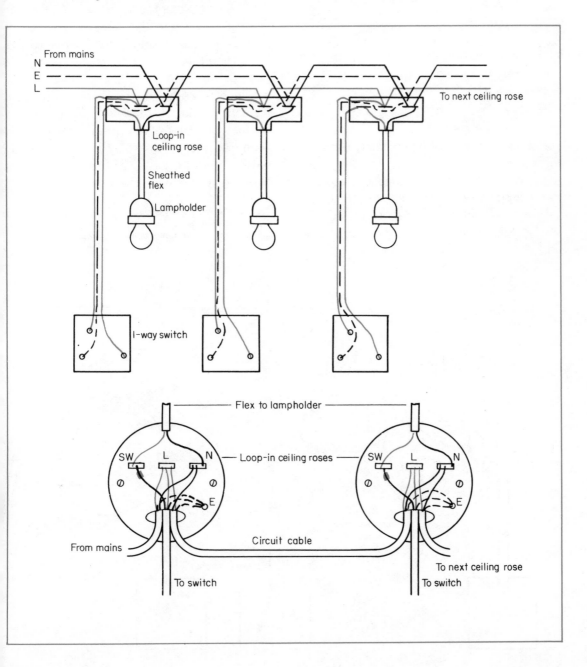

the same cable is run to the switch. The connections at the ceiling rose are shown in the illustration. Lighting points do not necessarily have to be wired in-line along the cable. Some may branch off from ceiling roses at any point but there is a limit to the number of cables a ceiling rose will comfortably accommodate.

The joint box system

With the joint box system the cable from the consumer unit runs to a series of joint boxes instead of to loop-in ceiling roses.

The joint box is often a 4-terminal type, one box being needed for each light and its switch and situated about midway between them. From the joint box, one length of twin and earth PVC sheathed cable is run to the light and another length to the switch.

Where two lights are in close proximity, and/or two switches form the one 2-gang

assembly, or there are three switches in an assembly, 5- and 6-terminal joint boxes are used instead of using two (or more) joint boxes. This can be seen from the illustration.

Combined loop-in and joint box circuits

A joint box is employed instead of a loop-in ceiling rose where the cable is run on the surface and also in situations where it would be difficult to loop a cable. Using a joint box simply means looping a cable out of a ceiling rose and running it to a joint box instead of direct to a lighting point. In normal situations the loop-in system is preferred because joint boxes are eliminated, they do not have to be fixed nor is time spent in making the joints.

The combined loop-in and joint box method of wiring a lighting circuit which is useful in many situations. The connections at joint boxes and ceiling roses are shown

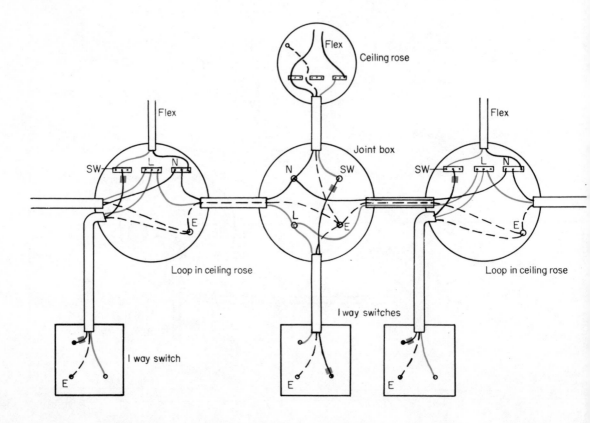

With the loop-in system all circuit joints are readily accessible at the ceiling rose, and also have the advantage that they are in the same room as the light and switch and not tucked out of the way under floorboards and floor coverings. This is of particular importance if a fault occurs and the circuit has to be tested and wires separated at the various joints.

Looping-in on lighting fittings

Where lighting fittings, other than plain pendants using a ceiling rose, are installed provision has to be made for the jointed live loop-in wires not attached to one of the flex cores. These live wires are jointed at an insulated connector which is either accommodated in the ceiling plate together with the connector joining the circuit wires to the flex of the fitting or, more likely, have to be housed in a box fixed into the ceiling above the ceiling plate of the fitting. For this a **BESA** circular box is used and has screw lugs for fixing the lighting fitting.

Wall light wiring

The loop-in system applies equally to wall light wiring. As the lights are fixed to the wall, it becomes difficult and costly to run two cables to each fitting, one looping in, the other looping out. Instead it is usually better to fix a joint box in the void above the ceiling of the room and from it run a twin and earth cable to each wall light point.

See under 'Fixing wall lights'.

Fixing joint boxes

Where a joint box is situated in the void between floorboards and ceiling or in the roof space it should be fixed to a piece of timber secured between two joists. This can be done as follows.

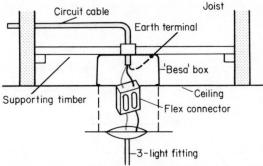

When a lighting fitting has a ceiling plate instead of a ceiling rose it is usually necessary to fit a conduit box into the ceiling to house the connections and to support the fitting

Measure between the span of the joists and cut a piece of 100 mm X 20 mm timber of the appropriate length. Secure this between the two selected joists about half way from the tops. Fix the joint box to the timber using wood screws, and check that the joint box will clear the floor-board when laid.

Fixing wall lights

A wall light is fixed by its baseplate either to a box sunk into the wall or it is fixed direct to the wall. The box, termed **'BESA'** box, is a termination box to contain the ends of the circuit wires from which the sheath is removed, and a flex connector which joints the wires to the flex of the fitting.

Only wall lights having a baseplate with 50 mm (2 in) fixing centres to match the lugs in the box can be mounted on this circular box. Most wall lights have other types of baseplate of which there are many shapes and sizes. These generally will not cover the circular box nor can they be fixed to it. As a box is essential to contain the ends of cables and wires and the flex connector, another type of box is used. This is a narrow metal box designed for use with architrave switches. The base-plate covers the box, which is sunk in the wall and the wall light is fixed to the wall itself in plugged holes.

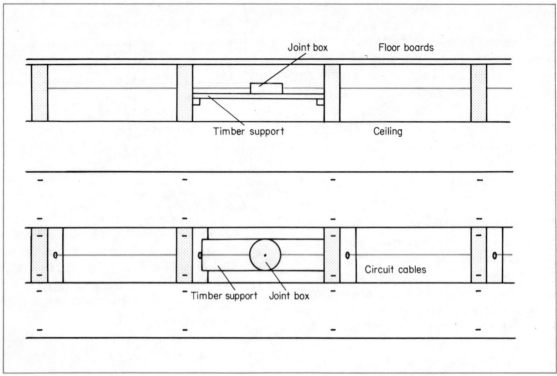

Joint box   Floor boards

Timber support   Ceiling

Circuit cables

Timber support   Joint box

A joint box in the void between the ceiling and floor-boards is mounted on a piece of timber fixed between the joists as shown

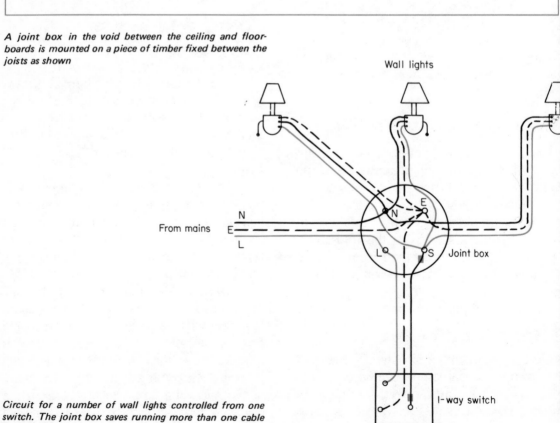

Wall lights

From mains

N
E
L

E
N
L   S   Joint box

I-way switch

Circuit for a number of wall lights controlled from one switch. The joint box saves running more than one cable to any wall light

Slide-on wall lights

One lighting fitting maker produces a range of wall lights which have a special base-plate in two sections. One section is a backplate with socket terminal connections for the circuit wires and is fixed to the wall. The other section forms the base-plate of the fitting and contains two contact pins which plug into the socket tubes of the backplate.

   The fitting slides on to the fixed back-plate and can be detached at any time (for cleaning) by sliding it off.

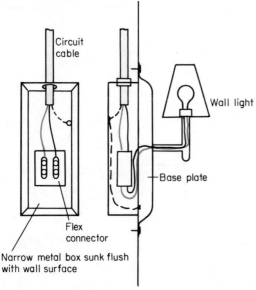

Wall lights have baseplates of various shapes and sizes and require a narrow architrave switch mounting box sunk into the wall to house the wires and connector

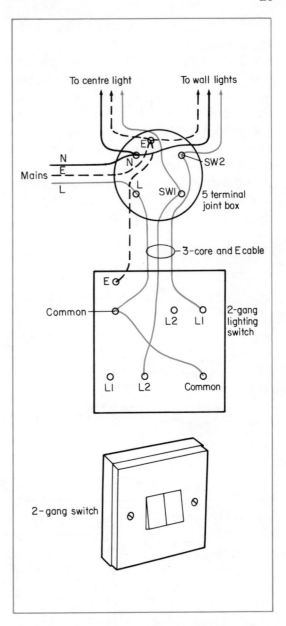

The circuit wiring where two lights or two sets of lights such as wall lighting and ceiling lighting are to be controlled separately from a 2-gang switch

Switching a light from two positions

To switch a light from two different positions a 2-way switching circuit is installed. There are a number of ways of doing this but the most simple is to wire the light as for one way switching. Connect the cable to the first switch and from this switch run 3-core and earth cable to the second switch position. At each position fit a 2-way switch.

With this method two cables run down the wall to the switch. One is the 2-core and earth sheathed cable, the other is the 3-core and earth sheathed cable. Both cables are run side by side in the one chase cut into the wall and are plastered over using plaster filler.

Two lights switched at one position

Where two lights are switched from one position, for example the ceiling light and wall lights to be switched from the entrance door, the two switches can be a 2-gang assembly mounted on a one gang box and supplied by a 3-core and earth PVC sheathed cable. Where both switches of a 2-gang unit are 2-way switches but both are used as one way switches, only two of the three terminals of each switch are used.

In the hall where the 2-way switch for the landing shares the same assembly with the hall light one-way switch, one is used for 2-way operation and the other for one way operation. With this arrangement, two 2-core (and earth) cables are needed because of the extra wire for the 2-way switch.

With this arrangement it is essential that the hall light and the landing light are supplied from the same circuit.

A 2-way switching circuit (a) the conventional circuit now used only in all-conduit installations; (b) the method used in sheathed cable installations in the home

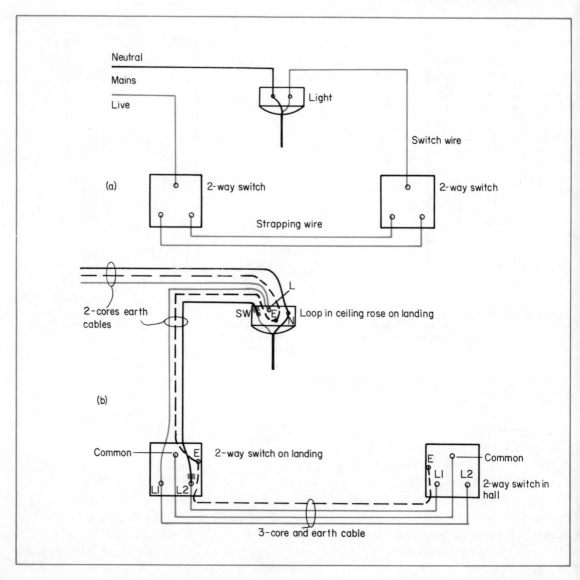

Switching a light from three (or more) positions

A light can be switched from three positions by fitting a special 4-terminal switch in a 2-way switching circuit. The switch, termed an intermediate switch, is connected at any point in the cable linking the 2-way switches as shown in the diagram.

Further switch positions can be made by adding more intermediate switches, one for each additional switch position.

When one of the switches of a three-switch circuit is to be a cord operated ceiling switch, the ceiling switch must be one of the two 2-way switches. This is because there are no intermediate ceiling switches. In practice the ceiling switch is usually the last switch in the circuit, as in the diagram, and connected to the one cable.

An intermediate switching circuit for controlling a light (or lights) from three positions. For control from four (or more) positions additional intermediate switches are inserted into the circuit

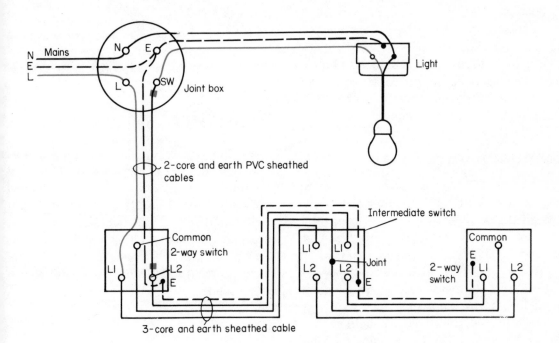

Chapter 4
Lamps

The amount of light given out or produced by an electric lamp — bulb, striplight or fluorescent tube — depends on the type of lamp and its wattage. The light produced is measured in lumens and a bulb or tube of a given wattage produces an average output of so many lumens. This will continue throughout most of its life.

Equally important is the number of lumens produced for each watt consumed, so it is usual to say, when comparing types, that a bulb or tube produces so many lumens per watt. The more the lumens per watt, the higher the efficiency of the lamp.

Comparison of lamp efficiencies

The electric light bulb operates at a fairly low efficiency whereas the fluorescent tube operates at a much higher efficiency at least three times that of the bulb. It is because of the inherent low efficiency of the bulb that there has been so much scope for improvement.

The efficiency of an electric light bulb is in the region of 25%; the remainder of the power consumed being emitted in heat. A bulb is really an illuminous heater and is often used as such. On the other hand, a fluorescent tube is cool in comparison; though the coolness of the glass is partly due to the fact that there is more glass in a bulb of given wattage and the heat is distributed over a wider surface area.

The luminous output of a fluorescent tube also varies with its 'colour'; the 'white' tube having a light output double that of the 'artificial daylight' tube for the same watts consumption. However, provided a tube of a given wattage produces sufficient light of the right colour in a room, variation in lumens output of the different colours is of little concern. This is not so with bulbs, where you may need to have one of higher wattage to get adequate light for the purpose, and therefore consume more electricity.

Types of electric light bulb

The ordinary electric light bulb is made in two principal types and in a wide range of wattages. The two types are single-coil and coiled-coil. The coiled-coil produces more light than a single-coil for a given wattage. Where possible it is therefore wise to choose a coiled-coil type.

Single-coil bulbs

These are made in about a dozen sizes ranging from 15 W to 1500 W though in the home the 150 W bulb is the largest normally used. This latter is also the largest type made with a bayonet cap to enable it to fit an ordinary lampholder (see Table 5a). Some variants are plain, pearl and pink pearl, conventional bulb shape and mushroom shape.

Coiled-coil bulbs

The coiled-coil type is limited to five wattages: 40 W, 60 W, 75 W, 100 W and 150 W, and is available in plain and pearl versions for all four sizes. It is not made in mushroom shape nor in pink pearl 'colour'. If, therefore, you require sizes other than those listed above you must buy single-coil lamps.

Coloured bulbs

Coloured bulbs of conventional size and shape are made in the colours: amber, blue,

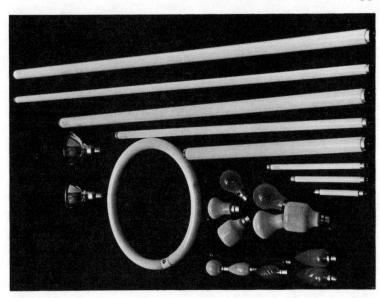

Selection of Osram bulbs and fluorescent tubes

green, pink, white, yellow and red, and in 15 W, 25 W, 40 W, 60 W, 100 W and 150 W sizes. The 15 W and 25 W types are suitable for outdoor use, but other sizes must be enclosed for protection against the rain. Most, but not all the colours, are available in the larger wattages.

Round bulbs of 15 W and 25 W, in various colours, are available for festive purposes together with other shapes.

Candle lamps

Plain and twisted candle lamps are made in 25 W, 40 W and 60 W sizes and in pearl, plain, amber and silvered colours. They are made in bc (bayonet cap) and sbc (small bayonet cap) versions.

These are used for wall lights and for period pendant fittings.

Tubular lamps (strip lights)

These are sometimes called 'strip lights' and are non-fluorescent, being tungsten filament lamps. There are two versions, one type is commonly used for applications in the home, and the second type is known as 'architectural lamps'.

The first type is available in double or single cap versions and used with special reflector type fittings as bedhead lights, mirror lights, etc. They are available in 30 W and 60 W sizes and may be clear, opal or amber.

Architectural lamps are made in two versions, straight and circular. The straight type is available in various wattages in opal finish and the curved version is made in eighth, quarter and half circle sizes in 60 W with opal finish.

Architectural lamps have peg type lamp caps and can be fixed to walls and ceilings without any fitting other than the two lampholders.

Sealed beam reflector lamps

These lamps made in 100 W and 150 W sizes are used as spot and floodlights and suitable for both outdoors and indoors. For outdoor use, special waterproof lampholders are required for attachment to walls and other structures or with spikes for insertion in the lawn or border soil. The lamps are available in clear type and various other colours.

Long life lamps

The ordinary electric light bulb has an average expected life of 1000 light hours when used in normal situations. This is the longest life possible with the optimum efficiency. Increase in light output will mean a reduction in the expected life.

Any increase in life means a corresponding drop in efficiency and therefore of lumens output per watt consumed. To obtain the equivalent wattage of the conventional bulb, means higher consumption of electricity. Some longer life bulbs are made which have an average expected life of 2000 hours; twice that of the ordinary bulb.

It is a personal choice as to whether it is better to have your bulbs last longer or to use less electricity for the same light output. You should have regard to the current price of electricity when compared with the cost of replacing bulbs and, in some situations, the inconvenience of replacing a bulb.

The fluorescent tube

The fluorescent tube is made in a large number of straight versions of various lengths and wattage, in four sizes of circular tube and one of 'U' shape.

The lengths of straight tubes range from 450 mm (18 in) of 15 W rating to 2400 mm (8 ft) of 125 W rating. There are also miniature fluorescent tubes of small diameter in four lengths and wattages ranging from 150 mm (6 in) of 4 W to 830 mm (21 in) of 13 W.

How a fluorescent tube works

A fluorescent lamp consists of a glass tube filled with mercury vapour and coated with fluorescent powder on its inside surface. At each end of the tube is an electrode consisting of a tungsten wire or braided filament coated with electron emitting material. The ends of the electrode are connected to a bi-pin lamp cap, or in the 5 ft 80 W version, to a bc conventional lamp cap and now available in a bi-pin version as an alternative.

When the lamp is operating, electrons flow along the tube from one electrode to the other. These electrons bombard the fluorescent powder on the tube surface causing it to produce light in a similar manner to a picture appearing on a television screen.

To start the flow of electrons a very high voltage is required, this being produced by a canister starter switch in conjunction with a choke. The starter switch has a make-and-break device which, when opened, creates a surge of very high voltage. This discharges between the electrodes in a manner similar to a motor car engine at the sparking plugs. Once started the flow of electrons continues, the current being restricted by the choke which now functions as a ballast.

The starter switch has another function — to pre-heat the electrodes by sustaining a current flow until the points open. This is the reason for the short delay on switching on a fluorescent light and the tube 'striking'.

Quick start tubes

Some fluorescent fittings have no starter switch(s) for the tubes. Instead there is a transformer to provide the prewarming and the tube itself has a metal stripe running throughout its length from one lamp cap to the other. The lamp caps are earthed at the lampholders.

This assists in the starting of the electron flow and, as there is no starter to operate, the lamp strikes without the characteristic delay of the switch-start type.

Fluorescent lighting circuit. (a) the switch-start circuit which includes a replaceable canister starter. (b) the quick-start circuit which needs no separate starter. (c) a twin-tube circuit

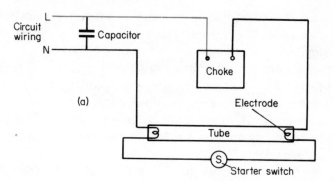

(a)

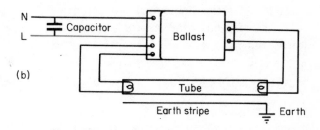

(b)

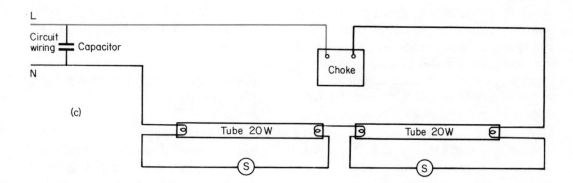

(c)

Tube life

A fluorescent tube has an expected life of 5000 to 7000 light hours or up to seven times that of an electric light bulb. The actual life of a tube is shortened by frequent switching on and off because each time the tube is switched on some of the coating on the electrodes is eroded, but with such a long life — about ten years — with average use any shortening of the life of a tube is hardly noticed.

A quick-start tube on a starterless circuit has a shorter life than a switch-start tube because more active material is eroded from the electrodes, but the life is still in the 7000-hour region.

Choosing the correct tube

The length of tube chosen depends to a large extent on the fitting chosen. The 4 ft 40 W type in either single- or double-tube version is a useful size for the kitchen. One 40 W tube gives a light output in excess of that from a 100 W bulb and with less than half the electricity consumption.

For reception rooms, hall, bathroom and other areas the smaller tubes are usually adequate and preference is often shown for the circular tube contained in an attractive fitting. For pelmet lighting, and other lighting where the tubes are hidden, the 5 ft 65 W or 80 W tube should be considered. For a long pelmet the 8 ft 125 W tube may be the better choice.

In the garage one or more 5 ft 80 W tubes of a high light output 'colour' will give the best light for car repairs. Mini-tubes are suitable as strip lights but usually come with the fittings, for example a shaving mirror light.

Colour range of fluorescent tubes

Fluorescent tubes are available in an extensive range of 'colours' but only a few of these are acceptable in the home for which warmer colours are recommended. Colour rendering is also important so that the colours of objects and materials are not too distorted. The most popular colour is de-luxe Warm White and this is chosen for living rooms in conjunction with filament lamps.

Where maximum light output is required, such as in a kitchen, White or Warm White should be chosen but with the sacrifice of some colour rendering. There is also available a colour which is used where a warmer colour than from filament lamps is required. These are sold under various trade names and, in addition to giving a warm colour, have good colour rendering qualities.

For decorative lighting giving a very warm effect, you can choose a pink tube and accept its poor colour rendering. For the garage you can have White or Warm White but where accurate colour matching may be required you should choose Artificial Daylight, or Daylight, to blend with natural daylight.

Circular tubes are made in Warm White

only. This is generally considered to be the best all round colour for the home.

Fluorescent lighting circuits

The fluorescent fitting is connected to the same wiring as any other lighting fitting except that an earth is essential with the starter-less type. Modern lighting circuits have an earth conductor at each lighting point. An earth conductor should also be installed at every lighting point where the fitting is of metal. Where there is no earth at a point it is necessary to run a 1.5 mm² green insulated cable from the point to the earthing terminal at the consumer unit (refer to the notes on earthing in Chapter 1).

The internal wiring of the fluorescent fitting depends on the type of tube and whether it has one or two tubes. The three principal circuits are: switch-start circuits; quick-start circuits and twin-tube circuits.

Switches for fluorescent lighting

The normal wall switch one-way on/off and two-way are used with fluorescent lights but, because of the surge on starting, the switch must be capable of handling the current, otherwise the contacts of the switch will burn out.

The standard plate switch of good quality available from all leading makes is adequate for fluorescent lighting. There should be no problem except, possibly, with low quality switches.

Fluorescent tube faults and remedies

Unlike a bulb which burns out completely at the end of its useful life a fluorescent tube lingers on and behaves in a strange,

Table 4 FLUORESCENT TUBE FAULTS AND SYMPTOMS

Tube behaviour	Possible cause	Remedy
Tube appears to be completely dead	Blown fuse; faulty lampholder; broken tube electrode	Mend fuse; or check lampholder or fit new tube
Electrodes glow but tube makes no attempt to start	If white glow, faulty starter If red glow, tube end of life Earth connection of quick-start tube ineffective	Change starter Fit new tube Check earthing
Tube glows one end and makes attempts to start	Lampholder at dead end short-circuited or disconnected from wires or not making contact with lamp; or broken tube electrode	Check lampholder and connections or fit new tube
Tube makes repeated attempts to start	Faulty starter Low mains voltage Tube at end of useful life (especially when it has a shimmering light effect)	Fit new starter Try again later when mains voltage is normal Fit new tube
Tube lights at half normal brilliance	Tube at end of useful life	Fit new tube
New tube lights with shimmering effect	Tube not likely to be faulty	Wait for the effect to settle down and behave normally

Table 5a LIGHT OUTPUT OF LAMPS

Wattage	Single-coil light output (lumens)	Coiled-coil light output (lumens)
15	110	—
25	200	—
40	325	390
60	575	665
75	780	880
100	1160	1260
150	1960	2040

Table 5b LIGHT OUTPUT OF FLUORESCENT LAMPS

Wattage	Length mm	ft	Lumens White	de luxe Warm White
80	1500	5	4875	3730
65	1500	5	4425	2400
40	1200	4	2700	1500
30	900	3	2000	1450
20	600	2	1050	780
15	450	18 in	700	500

MINIATURE TUBES

Wattage	Length mm	ft	Lumens White	Warm White
13	525	21	730	730
8	300	12	340	360
6	225	9	225	245
4	150	6	150	150

though characteristic, manner. A new tube sometimes behaves similarly when first switched on but this ceases after a while.

A faulty starter, or other faults in the fitting, also cause a tube to behave strangely.

The most common faults and their remedy are given in Table 4, so you will know what to expect and what to do.

Chapter 5
Power circuits

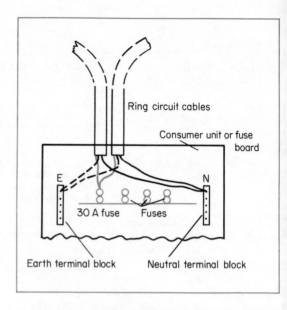

As mentioned in Chapter 1 the ring circuit is a domestic power circuit supplying a number of 13 A socket-outlets and fixed appliances situated within a floor area of 100 m² (1080 ft²). Cable used for this circuit is 2.5 mm² twin-core and earth PVC sheathed. The cable starts at a 30 A fuseway in the consumer unit, runs to the first socket-outlet, loops out of this to the next socket-outlet then to subsequent socket-outlets until it reaches the last. Here the cable is looped out and returns to the same 30 A fuseway in the consumer unit, thus completing a loop or ring.

Connections at the consumer unit

The two cables are connected at the fuse-way to the same terminals, i.e. red and red together, black and black together. The two earth conductors are connected to a terminal on the earthing strip, but being bare wires are first enclosed in green PVC sleeving to insulate and identify them.

Wiring remote socket-outlets

Socket-outlets situated off the main route of the cable do not have to be connected to the actual ring cable. Instead they are usually supplied from spur cables branching off the ring. These spurs are wired in the same size cable as that used for the ring.

Connections of the outward and return cables of a ring circuit. Both red wires go to the fuse terminal, the two blacks go to the neutral terminal block and the two earth conductors go to the earth terminal block

Connecting fixed appliances

Fixed appliances which may be connected to a ring circuit include skirting heaters, wall heaters, small water heaters and any non-portable electrical appliances having individual loadings of not more than 3000 W (13 A approx.).

Storage heaters for these are connected to separate time controlled circuits as described in Chapter 8. An immersion heater must not be supplied from a ring circuit, even though the loading is no more than 3000 W. The reason is that an immersion heater is classed as a continuous load and as such would reduce the effective capacity of the ring circuit; the primary function of the latter is to supply numerous appliances in use at various times during the day and night.

Connections of fixed appliances

A fixed appliance may be connected by its flexible cord to a fused plug and socket-

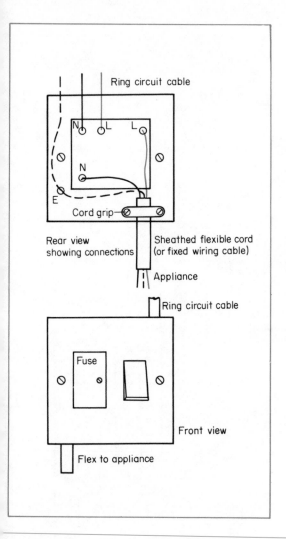

Ring circuit cable

N L L

N

E

Cord grip

Rear view
showing connections

Sheathed flexible cord
(or fixed wiring cable)

Appliance

Ring circuit cable

Fuse

Front view

Flex to appliance

Cable and flexible cord connections at a switched fused connection unit are shown in the diagram on the left. The red and black circuit wires go to the L and N terminals marked 'mains'. The brown and blue wires go to the remaining L and N terminals and the green sleeved circuit earth conductor and the green/yellow flex core go to the E terminals of the unit

(Below) Connecting spur cables to the ring circuit. (a) to the terminals of a 30 A 3-terminal joint box inserted into the ring cable and (b) to the terminals of an existing 13 A socket outlet

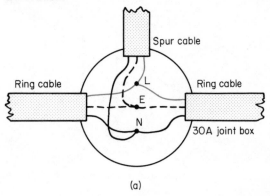

Spur cable

Ring cable

Ring cable

L

E

N

30A joint box

(a)

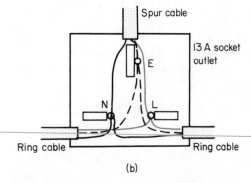

Spur cable

13 A socket
outlet

E

N

L

Ring cable

Ring cable

(b)

outlet but often it is more conveniently connected to a special fused outlet known as a fused connection unit. This used to be known as a fused spur unit.

The advantage of a fused connection unit is that the flex of the appliance is connected permanently to the unit, whereas when connected to a plug and socket-outlet someone might pull out the plug and use the socket for a portable appliance. Fused connection units are available with and without a switch and are available, if required, with a neon indicator.

Connecting spurs

A spur cable branching off a ring circuit may supply either one or two 13 A single socket-outlets, or one double socket-outlet, or one fixed appliance. Spurs from any one ring circuit are limited in number to the number of 13 A socket-outlets and fixed appliances actually wired into the ring cable.

If, therefore, there are eight socket-outlets wired into a ring circuit there may be up to a total of eight spurs branching

40

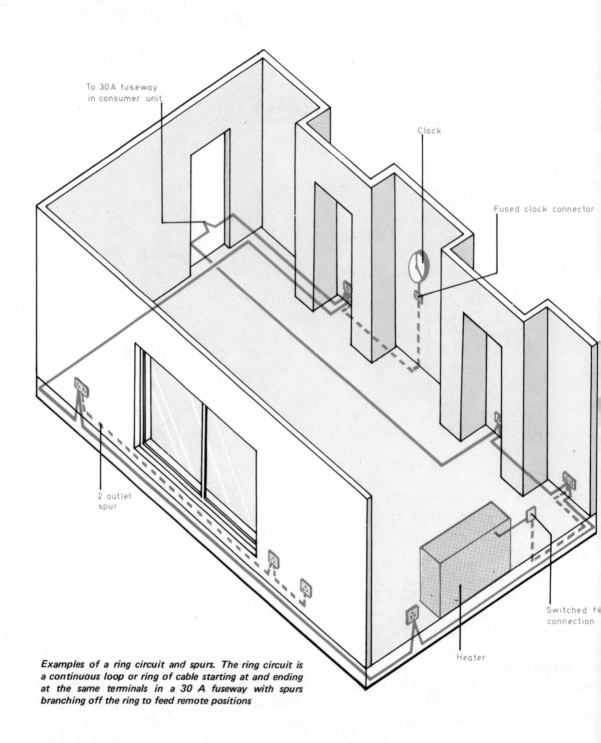

To 30A fuseway
in consumer unit

Clock

Fused clock connector

2 outlet
spur

Switched fu
connection

Heater

*Examples of a ring circuit and spurs. The ring circuit is
a continuous loop or ring of cable starting at and ending
at the same terminals in a 30 A fuseway with spurs
branching off the ring to feed remote positions*

off the ring. As each spur may supply two socket-outlets twice as many socket-outlets may be fed from spurs, as are connected to the ring cable itself. Where some of the spurs feed fixed appliances with only one on a spur, the number of spur fed socket-outlets will be less.

A spur cable may be connected to the ring cable either at the terminals of a ring socket or at a joint box wired into the ring cable at a convenient point. When adding spurs to a ring circuit it is usually better to insert a joint box into the cable under the floor rather than to break into an existing socket-outlet box. Also the terminals of a socket-outlet will not accommodate more than three cables — two for the looping ring cable and one for one spur.

Joint boxes used to connect spurs are of the 3-terminal 30 A type.

Fused spurs

A fused spur is a cable branching off a ring circuit similar to that of a conventional spur, except that the connection to the ring cable is at a fused connection unit (fused spur unit) instead of being solidly connected to the cable at a joint box or at the terminals of a ring socket-outlet. A fused spur can supply one or more socket-outlets, but as the total current demand of the points served by a fused spur must not exceed 13 A, only one 13 A socket-outlet can be supplied from a fused spur.

A number of sockets of lower rating may be connected to supply portable lights and small appliances. For instance, two 5 A 3-pin or six 2 A 3-pin sockets.

Electric clocks

Mains electric clocks may be supplied from a ring circuit. The connection to the clock must be made at a special fused connection unit called a clock connector.

The clock connector is in two portions, one being fixed and connected to the circuit wires and the other being a form of fused plug. This is connected to the flex of the clock and secured in the fixed portion by a captive screw to prevent anyone accidentally pulling it out and stopping the clock. The fuse is usually 3 A, but sometimes a 2 A fuse is fitted.

Clock points can be supplied from spurs. Where there is more than one clock point, a fused spur is preferred and the fused connection unit at the ring cable would be a non-switched version. Clock connectors can be flush or surface mounted. The flush type can be fixed behind a wall-mounted clock.

Height of fused connection units

There is no regulation height for fused connection units. The best position is close to the appliance it serves so that the flex is as short as possible.

Some appliances are connected to the fused connection unit by fixed wiring. This should be only a short length so that anyone working on the appliance is within reach of the switch of the connection unit.

Height of socket-outlets

The recommended height of a socket-outlet is not less than 150 mm (6 in) above the floor or above a working surface such as in a kitchen or above a sideboard in the dining room. Low mounted sockets in a room fitted with deep skirting boards should not be mounted on the skirting even if the skirting is more than 150 mm deep. In this position they have less protection from cleaning tools or from heavy furniture when being moved.

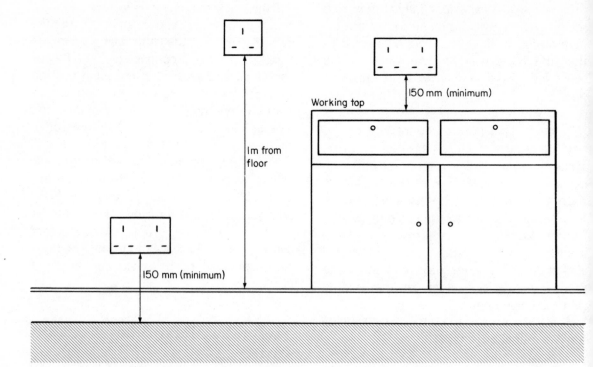

Socket outlets should be fixed at least 150 mm above the floor level and above a working surface such as in a kitchen. Where there are invalids and elderly persons a height of 1 m above floor level is recommended

Where a room is occupied by elderly people or invalids a height of 1 m (3 ft) for the socket-outlets is recommended. This means that one does not have to bend down to switch a socket on and off or to insert or withdraw a plug.

Bathroom shaver sockets

The shaver supply unit may be connected direct to the ring cable or from a spur cable without the need for a fuse in the spur. It may be installed in any position in the bathroom for although the unit may embody a switch, regulations permit it to be installed within reach of a person using a the bath or shower. This is the only switch where this applies.

Normally the unit will be fitted in the most convenient position for shaving which will be adjacent to the bathroom mirror. In many instances the unit will be out of reach of the bath but the regulations take into account that this is not always possible in the small bathroom of the average house.

Shaver sockets are also available for rooms other than the bathroom. As these have no isolating transformer they sell at a much lower price but must not on any account be fitted in a bathroom. (see page 78).

Garage and outdoor socket-outlets

Socket-outlets installed in the garage can be the same as installed in the house. Where there is a risk that they may be damaged, a metalclad version should be installed. The socket-outlets may be connected to the house ring circuit only if the garage is

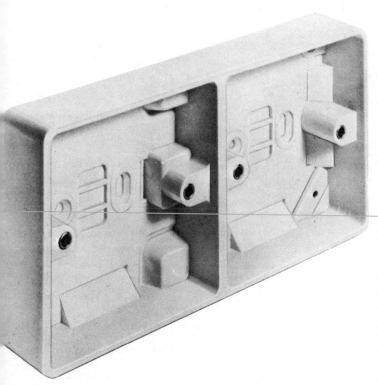

The various mounting boxes for socket outlets, fused connection units in 1- and 2-gang versions and for 20 A double pole switches, clock connectors and flexible cord outlets and other 'square-plate' accessories

44

attached to the house or is an integral construction. A detached garage needs a separate electricity supply, see Chapter 9.

Outdoor socket-outlets may be required for mowers, hedge-trimmers and other garden power-operated tools. These socket-outlets may be fixed to the outside wall of the house or on posts or other structures in the garden. They are normally of weatherproof pattern but there is now available a weatherproof cover which fits over the conventional socket-outlet to enable these to be used outdoors.

Radial power circuits

A radial power circuit is the name given to a circuit supplying a number of 13 A socket-outlets and fixed appliances using one cable which is not wired in the form of a ring but terminates at the last outlet.

The permitted number of socket-outlets (and fixed appliances) depends on the current rating of the circuit which can be either 20 A, wired in 2.5 mm² cable, or 30 A wired in 4 mm² cable. The number of socket-outlets and fixed appliances which can be served by a 20 A radial circuit depends also on the location of the circuit and whether the outlets are confined to one room.

Types of radial power circuit

There are, in effect, three types of radial power circuit. A 20 A circuit supplying more than one room; a 20 A circuit supplying one room only and a 30 A radial circuit supplying one or more rooms.

Two-room 20 A radial circuit

This circuit can have a maximum of two 13 A socket-outlets (or fixed appliances) each in a different room, hall, landing or other service area. It is wired in 2.5 mm² 2-core and earth cable starting at a 20 A fuseway used solely for that circuit.

One-room 20 A radial circuit

This circuit is also wired in 2.5 mm² cable from a 20 A circuit fuseway and may supply up to a maximum of six 13 A socket-outlets and fixed appliances. This is provided they are all in the one room of an area not exceeding 30 m² (300 ft²) and that the room is not a kitchen and none of the appliances is a fixed water heater.

(a) a 20 A radial circuit for two singles or one double 13A socket outlets. (b) a 30 A radial circuit which may supply up to six 13 A socket outlets and fixed appliances

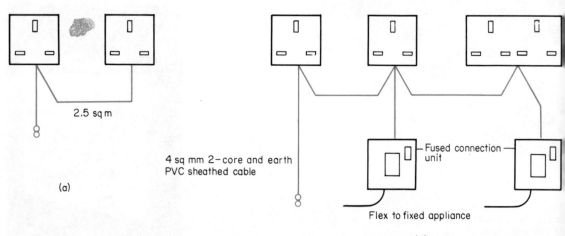

2.5 sq m

4 sq mm 2-core and earth PVC sheathed cable

(a)

Fused connection unit

Flex to fixed appliance

(b)

30 A radial circuit

This is wired in 4 mm² 2-core and earth PVC sheathed cable from a 30 A fuseway. It may supply up to a maximum of six 13 A socket-outlets and fixed appliances but without the restrictions applying to a 20 A radial circuit. The socket-outlets and fixed appliances (if any) may be installed in any rooms and service areas and the fixed appliances may be of any type having individual loadings not in excess of 3 kW. This circuit is excellent as a supplementary to a ring circuit and particularly suitable for a fully equipped kitchen to lighten the load on the ring circuit; especially where the kitchen is also used as the home laundry.

The 15 A power plug system

Before the advent of the ring circuit and its associated 13 A fused plugs and socket-outlets, the 'power system' consisted of 15 A round-pin plugs and socket-outlets, each wired from a separate circuit.

Forthcoming changes

With the introduction of the *IEE Wiring Regulations* 15th edition in early 1981, circuits using 13 A socket outlets are expected to include the following changes.

In ring circuits, a spur cable may supply either one single or one double socket outlet or one fixed appliance, but not two single sockets as at present.

A radial circuit may supply any number of socket outlets, but the maximum floor area served by a 30 A radial circuit will be 50 m² and a 20 A radial circuit 20 m². A 30 A radial circuit may be wired in 4 mm² cable, but the protective device must be either a cartridge fuse or a miniature circuit breaker, not a rewirable fuse as at present.

The 5 A socket-outlet

The 5 A round pin plug and socket-outlet was also used extensively in dwellings, these too being in 2-pin and 3-pin versions. They were intended mainly for small appliances of up to 1000 W.

One 5 A socket-outlet was supplied from a 5 A circuit, two from a 10 A and three from a 15 A circuit but, in many instances, more than one 5 A socket-outlet was supplied from a 5 A circuit. The 2 A plug and socket-outlet was installed especially for table lamps, floor standards and other portable lighting and are still installed for this type of lighting.

As each socket has an assumed maximum load of ½ A (equivalent to 120 W on 240 V supplies) up to a maximum of ten 2 A socket-outlets may be connected to a 5 A circuit exclusively used for the socket-outlets. The 2 A socket-outlet is also supplied from a lighting circuit, but it must be assessed at 120 W when adding up the lighting load.

Round-pin plug adaptors

Because of the scarcity of 15 A sockets on the old radial wiring system, plug adaptors were used extensively on these circuits. Principally they were to enable 5 A and 2 A plugs to be used from the 15 A sockets but the adaptors also enabled two 15 A plugs to be used from one 15 A socket-outlet.

The use of multi-plug adaptors is bad practice as, apart from a risk of overloading a socket-outlet, long flexes have to be used which are themselves a hazard.

The radial system

The numerous 15 A circuits radiating from a central fuseboard are known collectively as the radial system. This system is now superceded by the ring circuit. It has no connection with the modern radial power circuit.

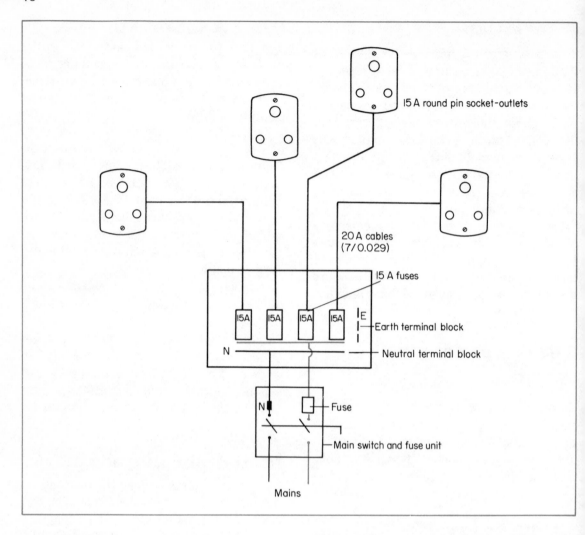

20 A cables
(7/0.029)

15 A round pin socket-outlets

15 A fuses

E
Earth terminal block

N
Neutral terminal block

N
Fuse

Main switch and fuse unit

Mains

The old radial system of wiring power (15 A) socket outlets where a separate circuit from a fuse unit is required for each 15 A outlet

Circuits for conversion

Where only one 15 A socket-outlet is on a circuit this may be replaced by a 13 A type. Two may be replaced provided the circuit cable is 7-strand and that the fuse can be uprated to 20 A.

If there are more than two 15 A socket-outlets on a circuit, conversion is not permitted and the circuit should be scrapped. Because of the old wiring, attempts to change the sockets will almost certainly result in the insulation breaking off the conductor. The only satisfactory solution is to rewire by installing a ring circuit.

Conversion to 13 A socket-outlets

Most 15 A socket-outlets can be replaced by the modern 13 A socket-outlet. When replacing a 15 A socket-outlet by a 13 A type, check that there is an earth wire at the outlet. If not, it is necessary to run an earth conductor from the socket-outlets to the consumer unit using 2.5 mm² green PVC insulated cable. The 15 A 2-pin and 3-pin socket-outlets often will not have an earth.

Chapter 6
Circuit for electric cookers

Small table cookers and other portable appliances having individual loadings not in excess of 3 kW are run off 13 A fused plugs and socket-outlets. They require no special wiring though extra socket-outlets may be needed in the kitchen when additional electrical cooking appliances are bought. These additional socket-outlets may be served from the ring circuit and spurs.

Family-size cookers, whether free-standing or built-in split-level, need an exclusive circuit from a fuseway of appropriate current rating.

A table cooker of up to 3000 W rating may be supplied from a 13 A socket outlet on the ring circuit or from a 15 A socket outlet of an old radial circuit

Current ratings of circuits

Most electric cookers have a total loading of about 12 kW or less and are supplied by a 30 A circuit, wired in 6 mm² cable (or, sometimes 4 mm² cable) from a 30 A fuseway. The cable terminates at a cooker control unit or switch of 50 A current rating.

Large-size family cookers, usually with loadings in excess of 12 kW are supplied from a 45 A circuit wired in 6 mm², or 10 mm² cable from a 45 A fuseway but terminated at the same 50 A cooker control unit or switch as the 30 A circuit cable. This is because the switchgear makers have designed the control units for the higher current demand.

Cooker control units

The conventional cooker control unit consists of a double-pole switch and a switched socket-outlet for an electric kettle. Some units have a neon indicator for the cooker switch and also for the kettle. The unit can be either flush- or surface-mounted.

An alternative to a combined unit is a

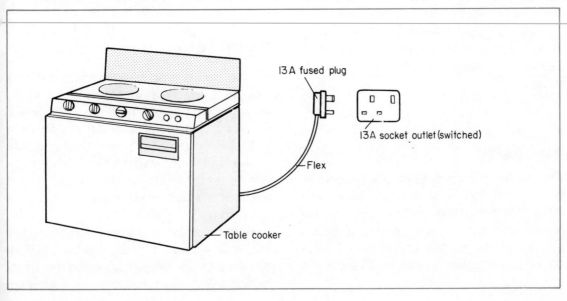

13 A fused plug

13 A socket outlet (switched)

Flex

Table cooker

cooker control double-pole switch (with or without neon indicator) but which does not incorporate a kettle socket-outlet.

Cooker current demand

If the total current of a 12 kW electrical appliance used on 240 V is calculated by dividing 12,000 by 240, then the result will be 50 A. If you add to this figure, 12 A for a 3 kW electric kettle plugged into the socket-outlet of a cooker control unit, you get a total of 62 A which is the total current rating of a 12 kW family size cooker and kettle.

A cooker of the above rating is, in fact, supplied from a 30 A circuit which at first sight does not make sense though complying with the regulations. The reason for the apparent discrepancy is that the regulations have assumed a current demand based on the known fact that not all boiling plates, grill and oven of a cooker, and also the kettle are in use at the same time.

Even on those rare occasions, such as cooking the Christmas dinner, when everything may be switched on for a time, the thermostat of the oven and the variable controls of boiling plates and the grill reduce the actual current demand. The regulations have therefore introduced a diversity factor for calculation assessed or assumed demand for domestic electric cookers.

Calculating cooker diversity

The assumed demand for an electric cooker is based on 100 % of the first 10 A, plus 30 % of the remaining current, plus 5 A for an electric kettle socket-outlet if incorporated in the control unit. For a 12 kW cooker plus kettle the assumed demand is as follows:

Total current of cooker: 50 A	
100 % of first 10 A	10
30 % of remaining 40 A	12
Kettle socket	5
Total assumed current	27

The current rating for the circuit supplying the cooker is therefore 30 A.

Circuit cable route

The cable running from the circuit fuse to the cooker control unit takes the shortest possible path. This is usually under the floorboards and up the wall to the control unit.

If the floor is solid, as in many kitchens, the cable is taken up the wall through the ceiling into the void beneath the boards (or roof space if a bungalow) and down the wall to the control unit. The cable may be run on the surface or be buried in the plaster. If run on the surface, cable with white sheathing is usually chosen.

The cooker control unit is normally situated at a height of about 1.5 m (5 ft) from the floor and preferably to one side of the cooker. It must be within 2 m (6 ft) of the cooker it controls.

Types of control unit

Of the two principal types of cooker control unit, the type incorporating a kettle socket-outlet is the more popular. Since, however, it is important that the kettle is not used on the cooker hob where its flex would trail over a switched-on boiling plate it is better to have the unit without a socket where it has to be fixed immediately above the cooker.

Cooker control units incorporating a kettle socket-outlet were introduced before the days of the ring circuit when one other 'power plug' was the 'Norm' in a kitchen.

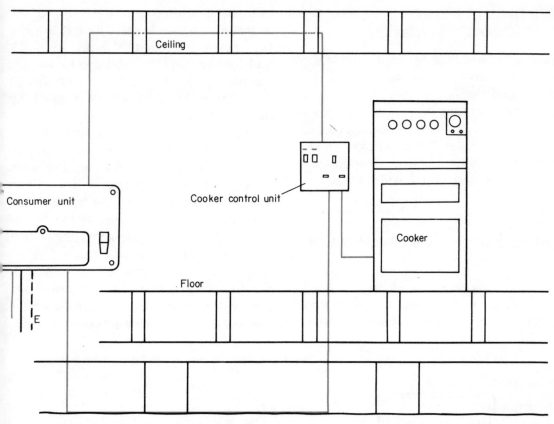

Ceiling

Consumer unit

Cooker control unit

Cooker

Floor

E

Alternative routes for a cable of a cooker circuit running from the fuseway in the consumer unit to the control switch adjacent to the cooker. If the kitchen floor is solid the cable can usually be run in the void above the ceiling

New houses are usually wired to include a cooker circuit, and a 13 A socket outlet is fixed in place of the cooker control unit. To convert this back to a cooker circuit the socket outlet is replaced by a cooker control switch as shown

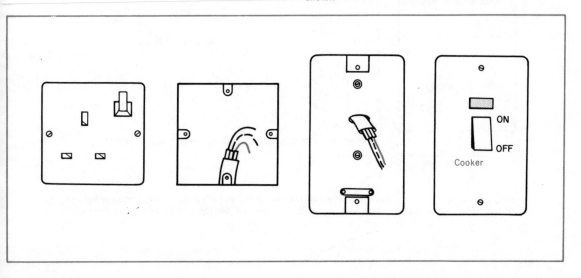

ON

OFF

Cooker

50

Replacing a socket-outlet with a control unit

Where a socket-outlet has been fixed at the end of a cooker circuit and a change to electric cooking is being made it is simply a question of replacing the socket-outlet by a cooker control switch. As mentioned above, if the socket-outlet is immediately above the cooker another socket-outlet above a working surface will be needed for the kettle.

Connecting a cooker to the control unit

The same type and size of cable is used both from the control unit to the cooker and for the circuit. For a free-standing cooker

this cable drops down the wall to the cooker with a free droop at the end to allow the cooker to be pulled away from the wall for cleaning. The cable end in the control unit or switch is well anchored though the upper section of the cable drop can be fixed to the wall with cable clips.

There is now available a terminal box which is fixed to the wall behind a free-standing cooker and breaks the cable from the control unit to the cooker. The section from the control unit to the terminal box is fixed and can be buried in the plaster and the final cable connecting the cooker to the terminal box remains free.

If the cooker is removed for repairs, or changed for a new model, the cooker section of the cable is disconnected from the box and the moulded plastic cover replaced.

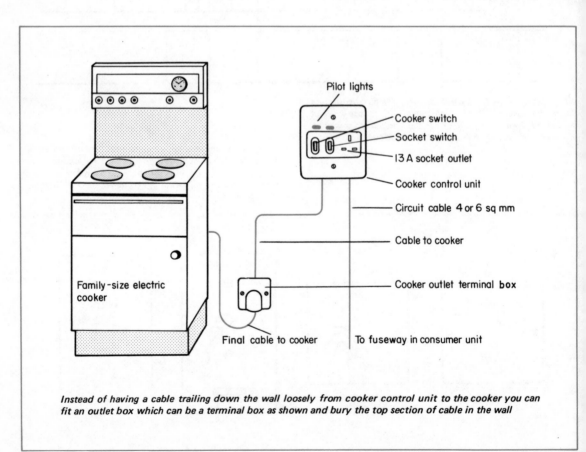

Instead of having a cable trailing down the wall loosely from cooker control unit to the cooker you can fit an outlet box which can be a terminal box as shown and bury the top section of cable in the wall

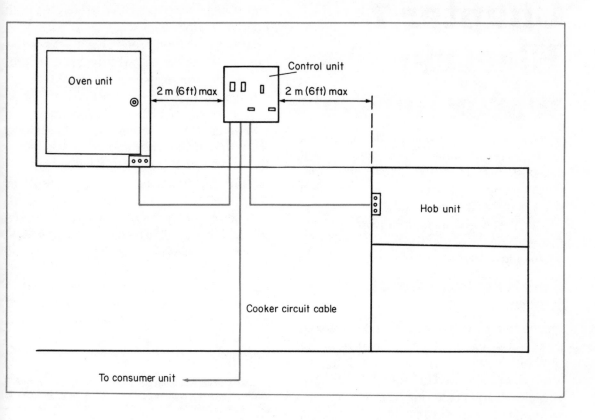

Oven unit

Control unit

2 m (6 ft) max

2 m (6 ft) max

Hob unit

Cooker circuit cable

To consumer unit

Reconnecting the cooker or connecting a new cooker takes only a few minutes.

An alternative is a cable outlet box which has no terminals. The cable is not cut but the section down the wall can be buried in the plaster.

Split-level cookers

A single circuit is used to supply the two sections of a split-level cooker and one cooker unit or control switch can be used for both provided neither is more than 2 m (6 ft) from the control. Usually both oven and hob sections are close together. If the sections are well apart and the control unit is situated midway, the sections can be up to 4 m (12 ft) apart and still be within the regulations. The control unit can be with or without a socket-outlet as desired.

The same type and size of cable is used between the control unit and the cooker sections as for the cooker circuit and the current demand is assessed as for a free-standing cooker. Each section can be supplied by a separate cable which means two cables from the control unit, one to the oven section, the other to the hob. Alternatively, one cable can be run from the control unit to the nearest section and from the terminals of this section another cable of the same size and type is run to the second section.

It is important that the same size of cable is used throughout as this is governed by the circuit fuse as well as by the actual current a section will need to carry. In other words, splitting a cooker into two sections does not permit any reduction in cable size.

Chapter 7
Electric
water heaters

Electric heating of water can be carried out in a variety of ways. These include small capacity heaters fitted above the sink, instantaneous sink heaters or immersion heaters in the hot water tank.

The selection and plumbing-in of water heaters is dealt with in the companion book *'Home Plumbing'*.

Small storage water heaters

Small storage water heaters fitted over the sink or washbasin having capacities of up to about 3 gallons and electrical loadings of 1 to 3 kW are usually supplied from the ring circuit by means of a spur. Except in a bathroom, the outlet can be a fused plug and switched socket-outlet, preferably with neon indicator.

The connection from plug to the water heater is heat-resisting 3-core flexible cord. In the bathroom, where no socket-outlets are permitted other than an approved shaver socket, a switched fused connection unit is used as the outlet. This should also have a neon indicator and be connected to the water heater by 3-core flexible cord.

The switch of the connection unit, as other wall switches, must be out of reach of a person using the bath or shower. Where this is impracticable a cord-operated ceiling switch is necessary and the outlet to the water heater should be a cord outlet unit. As there must be a fuse in the circuit, a non-switched fused connection unit can be fixed outside the bathroom at the point where the spur cable is connected to the ring circuit.

A small storage water heater having a loading not exceeding 3000 W may be supplied from a 13 A plug and socket outlet or fused connection unit connected to a spur from the ring circuit

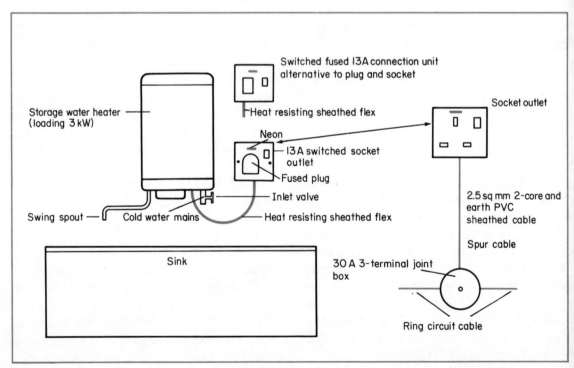

Storage water heater (loading 3 kW)

Swing spout — Cold water mains

Sink

Switched fused 13A connection unit alternative to plug and socket

Heat resisting sheathed flex

Neon

13A switched socket outlet

Fused plug

Inlet valve

Heat resisting sheathed flex

Socket outlet

2.5 sq mm 2-core and earth PVC sheathed cable

Spur cable

30 A 3-terminal joint box

Ring circuit cable

Immersion heaters

An immersion heater is classed as a continuous load and as such should not be supplied from a ring circuit since its 3 kW loading would deprive the ring circuit of nearly half of its 7.2 kW load capacity. Instead a separate circuit is used for the immersion heater which can be wired in 1.5 mm² PVC sheathed cable from a 15 A circuit fuse, or preferably in 2.5 mm² cable from a 20 A circuit fuse.

An essential requirement for an immersion heater circuit is a double-pole isolating switch which should be fixed within reach of the immersion heater so that anyone adjusting the thermostat with the terminal cover off has access to the isolator. For a single-element immersion heater this switch is a standard 20 A double-pole plate switch available with or without neon indicator and flex outlet facilities. Where required, the plate can be engraved **WATER HEATER**.

A 13 A fused plug and switched socket-outlet is sometimes used instead of a double-pole switch. Isolation is effected by pulling out the plug, but with a sustained 3 kW loading, a plug and socket tends to overheat especially in the vicinity of a hot water tank and even more so when enclosed in a tank cupboard. Where, as is often the case, a tank cupboard opens into the bathroom, a socket-outlet is prohibited as it could be misused by plugging in a portable appliance.

Although the water heater switch should be within reach of the immersion heater, it is essential that it cannot be reached by a person using the bath or shower. In these circumstances, either the switch must be fixed outside the bathroom or a cord operated ceiling switch is necessary.

A circuit feeding a single element immersion heater terminates at an on/off double pole 20 A switch and from this 3-core heat resisting flex runs to the immersion heater

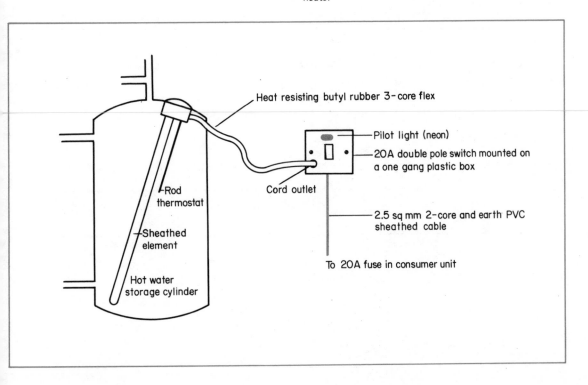

Heat resisting butyl rubber 3-core flex

Pilot light (neon)

20A double pole switch mounted on a one gang plastic box

Cord outlet

Rod thermostat

Sheathed element

Hot water storage cylinder

2.5 sq mm 2-core and earth PVC sheathed cable

To 20A fuse in consumer unit

Dual immersion heater

A dual immersion heater is designed for fitting into the top of a hot water storage cylinder and consists of two elements, one short and one long. The short element is for heating a small quantity of water for normal daily use, the long element is for heating the full contents of the tank when large amounts of hot water are required for a bath or other purposes.

Some models have an integral change-over switch mounted on the heater head to switch over from one element to the other. Immersion heaters without this integral switch require an external change-over switch wired into the circuit. The switch used for this is a combined 20 A double-pole switch and change-over switch fixed in the place of the ordinary isolating switch and connected to the immersion heater by heat-resisting flex. As an extra wire is required for the second element and 4-core flex is not generally available, it is usual to have two 3-core flexible cords as though for two separate elements but connected as shown in the diagram.

Remote control of immersion heater

When an immersion heater is switched on and off as hot water is needed and not in continuous operation, it is useful to have a remote control operated from the kitchen.

A special 2-point control is available for this arrangement, consisting of two double-pole switches, each with a neon indicator. One switch (the master switch) incorporates an isolator and is fitted at the immersion heater end; the other (auxiliary switch) is fitted in the kitchen. The immersion heater can be switched on and off by either

An immersion heater can be controlled from the kitchen as well as from the tank cupboard by installing a 2-point control system. The switch at the immersion heater end contains an isolator

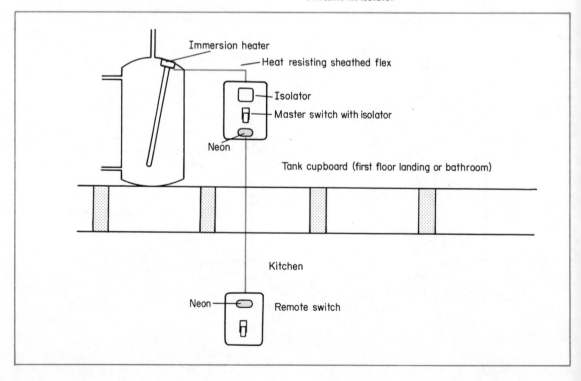

Immersion heater

Heat resisting sheathed flex

Isolator

Master switch with isolator

Neon

Tank cupboard (first floor landing or bathroom)

Kitchen

Neon

Remote switch

switch, both neon indicators going on and off when one switch is operated.

This arrangement is intended mainly for single-element immersion heater installations but can be used with dual immersion heaters with the changeover switch wired in between the master switch and the immersion heater. Another arrangement is to have a remote switch to control the long element only of a dual immersion heater so that, when extra hot water is needed, the long element can be switched into circuit from the kitchen.

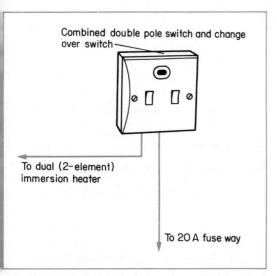

Combined double pole switch and change over switch

To dual (2–element) immersion heater

To 20 A fuse way

The two elements of a dual immersion heater are controlled by a change-over switch and double-pole isolating switch in a combined unit

Two-immersion heater installations

Where the hot water storage tank is rectangular or there is insufficient headroom to insert a top-entry immersion heater into a cylinder, side-entry immersion heaters are fitted.

An immersion heater fitted a few inches from the base heats the full contents of the tank but where only small quantities are normally run off during the day a second immersion heater is fitted. This is a few inches from the top of the tank, according to the dimensions of the tank and the amount of water to be heated. The top immersion heater will be fitted lower down from the top of a small-diameter cylinder than for a large rectangular tank.

Two immersion heaters operate similarly to one dual immersion heater and, if both have 3 kW loading, a change-over switch is used to change over from one to the other.

Off-peak operation

Where the white meter tariff is in operation it can be an advantage to heat the full contents of a tank overnight when the cheaper rate for electricity is in force and switch on the short element when additional hot water is needed.

This normally requires two circuits for the immersion heater installation. One circuit is used for the night rate supply, when time controlled in conjunction with night storage heaters, this supplying the long element of a dual immersion heater or the lower immersion heater of a two-immersion heater arrangement. The other circuit is from the unrestricted supply and, as it will be only for intermittent use, the circuit can be a spur of a ring circuit. For two immersion heaters, each is controlled separately but for a dual immersion heater a twin double-pole isolating switch is needed.

Automatic control

An immersion heater can be switched on and off automatically by means of a timeswitch. A timeswitch (e.g. the 'Imerset') has been designed especially for this purpose and gives a choice of two switch-on and switch-off periods each 24 hours. These can be programmed to suit the family's requirements but a common arrangement is to switch off the heater late at night, on early in the morning, off after breakfast as the

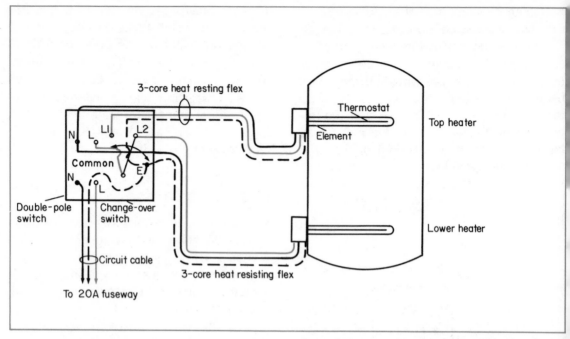

3-core heat resting flex

Thermostat

Top heater

Element

N L L1 L2

Common

E

N L

Double-pole switch

Change-over switch

Lower heater

Circuit cable

3-core heat resisting flex

To 20A fuseway

(Above) Two immersion heaters fitted into the one tank are controlled by a combined on/off double pole switch and a change over switch. A separate 3-core heat resisting flexible cord goes to each heater

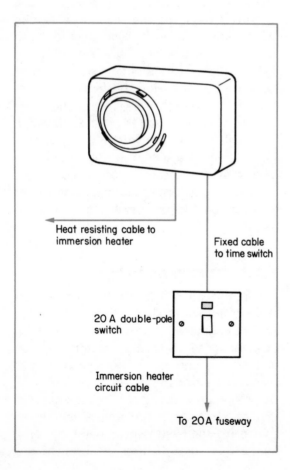

Heat resisting cable to immersion heater

Fixed cable to time switch

20 A double-pole switch

Immersion heater circuit cable

To 20A fuseway

The illustration on the left shows a special time switch inserted between the double pole switch and the immersion heater to provide switch-on periods to suit the family

family leaves for work, and on again just before the first member of the family returns home. Other manufacturers also have available similar timeswitches which are equally suitable. The purpose of the timeswitch is to save electricity by not keeping a tank of water hot when none is being drawn off.

Some timeswitches have an over-ride switch to enable current to be provided to the immersion heater out of programmed hours, such as over weekends. If the time-switch has no over-ride switch a 20 A double-pole switch can be fitted and con-nected to the timeswitch to bridge the open switch contacts of the timeswitch to obtain hot water out of hours.

The live pole of the double-pole switch bridges the single-pole contacts of the timeswitch and also supplies current to the neon indicator. The neutral pole merely supplies the neon indicator which needs both live and neutral poles to energise the neon.

The use of a timeswitch to cut off the current to an immersion heater overnight, and at other times, does not eliminate the need for lagging the tank. The lagging, which should be at least 100 mm (4 in) thick, reduces heat losses and conserves the hot water whether the heater is 'On' or 'Off'.

Instantaneous water heaters

Washbasins

Instantaneous water heaters having loadings of 3 kW fitted over the washbasin for hand washing can be supplied from a ring circuit spur. The connection at the water heater should be either a 13 A fused plug and socket-outlet or, as in a bathroom, a switched fused connection unit with the switch out of reach of a person using the bath.

Shower units

Instantaneous water heaters used as shower units have electrical loadings of 5 kW and 6 kW. These need separate 30 A circuits from 30 A fuseways in consumer units, the circuits being wired in 4 mm² 2-core and earth PVC sheathed cable. An isolating switch is needed with these water heater units and should be fixed within reach of the heater unit.

Where the shower unit is installed in the bathroom, there is usually difficulty in siting the switch out of reach of the fixed bath and out of reach of the person using the shower. To meet this situation a 30 A

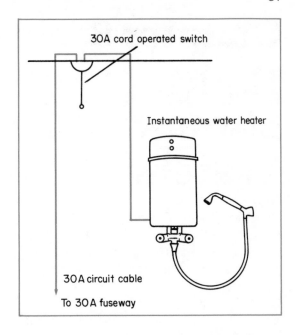

An instantaneous water heater of a shower unit is fed from a 30 A circuit and needs an isolating switch within reach, if possible, of the heater unit. To meet regulations this should be a 30 A cord operated ceiling switch as shown

double-pole cord-operated switch has been introduced. The circuit cable, therefore, runs from the fuseway in the consumer unit to the ceiling switch and from this to the water heater unit.

Sink water heaters

For the sink, a 5 kW version of the shower instantaneous water heater is available. The circuit is the same as for a shower unit but need be only of 20 A current rating using 2.5 mm² cable and a 20 A double-pole switch fitted near the water heater.

One version of this heater, having a loading of 7 kW can be used to supply two outlets — the shower and the sink or the shower and a washbasin — a special 2-way faucet tap being fitted for the purpose, since each outlet must be of the open type.

Chapter 8
Night storage heaters

Night storage heaters operate on the principle of thermal storage blocks being charged with heat during an overnight period when electricity is supplied at a lower price and releases the heat during the day when electricity is more expensive. Heat is stored during an 8-hour period starting at about 11 p.m. and ending at 7 a.m. the following morning. The times vary slightly between areas and some electricity boards have a 10-hour period starting at 9 p.m. An 8-hour period is sufficient to fully charge a heater.

Types of storage heating

The greatest proportion of night storage heating consists of individual storage heaters installed in the various rooms, though usually limited to the ground floor of a 2-storey dwelling.

Other forms of storage heating are:
(i) Floor warming where warming wires are embedded into the concrete of the floor, the concrete acting as the storage medium; and
(ii) A central heating system consisting of a large size storage heater situated in a central position and supplying the various rooms by warm air flowing through a duct system, or by a central boiler supplying hot water to a conventional radiator system. The warm air system is termed Electricaire; the hot water method is called Centrelec.

The individual night storage electric heaters are made in two principal types: storage radiators and storage fan heaters.

The electric storage radiator consists of a thermal storage block enclosed in a metal casing but separated from it by thermal insulation. Heat is emitted from the casing into the room by radiation, the rate of heat output being controlled by the thickness and quality of the thermal insulation determined at the design stage of the heater. An internal thermostat prevents excessive heat being stored and therefore determines the amount of heat stored during an overnight charge period. An input controller operated by the householder can reduce the amount charged.

Rate of heat output

The rate of heat output in kilowatts depends on the size of the heater. The larger the storage block, the more heat stored and therefore the greater the heat output the next day. Apart from varying the input of heat, the user has no control over the rate of heat output.

Makers of storage radiators reckon that a constant heat output is maintained for the first 10 hours after which the heat output tapers off. To counteract this tapering off some storage radiators incorporate booster devices which push out the remainder of the heat stored.

Sizes of storage radiator

Storage radiators have kilowatt loadings ranging from about 1¼ kW to about 3¼ kW, but these loadings do not represent the rate of heat output as do the loadings of direct acting heaters. The higher the loading the greater the storage capacity and the greater the amount of heat stored which in turn increases the rate of heat output.

This means that the kW loading serves as

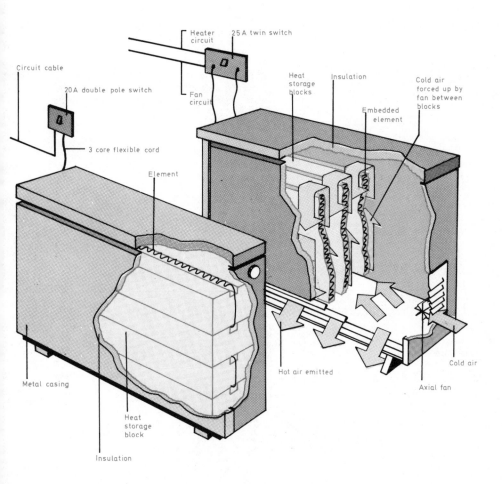

Circuit cable

20A double pole switch

3 core flexible cord

Heater circuit

25A twin switch

Fan circuit

Heat storage blocks

Insulation

Embedded element

Cold air forced up by fan between blocks

Element

Metal casing

Heat storage block

Insulation

Hot air emitted

Axial fan

Cold air

The picture on the left shows an interior view of an electric storage radiator. Storage radiators are usually supplied by separate 20 A circuits each of which terminates at a 20 A double-pole switch having a cord outlet for the 3-core flex to the heater

An interior view of a storage fan heater is shown in the illustration on the right. These are supplied from two circuits, one on the cheap night rate under time switch control for the heater, the other from the unrestricted supply for the fan

60

a guide which, together with the makers' data, enables you to choose the sizes best suited to your individual requirements.

Storage fan heaters

The storage fan heater is similar to the storage radiator, but incorporates a fan system which blows cold air over the heated storage block and expels the heated air through a grille into the room.

To reduce the radiated heat to almost nothing, the fan storage heater has much more thermal insulation. In effect, therefore, heat is emitted only when the fan is switched on, thus giving the user control of the output of the heat. Although the elements are switched on for the 8-hour overnight period only, the fan can be switched on at any time during the 24 hours because it is supplied from an ordinary unrestricted circuit.

By an arrangement of stub ducts and grilles, one storage fan heater can be sited to supply two or more adjoining rooms.

Circuit wiring for four storage radiators. Each circuit originates at a 20 A fuseway in the 4-way consumer unit under the control of the night-rate time switch

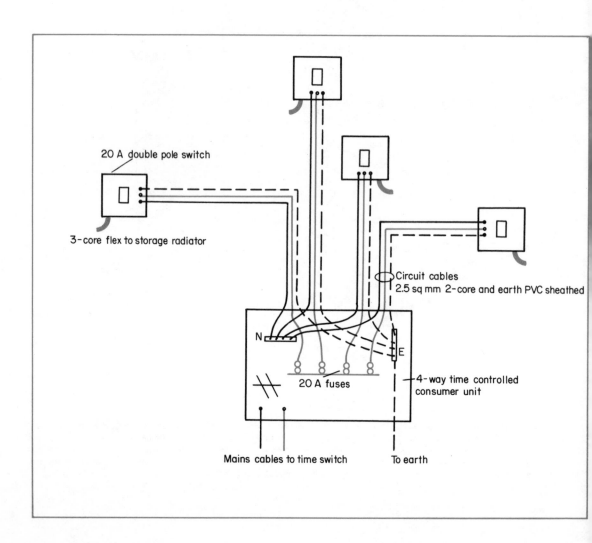

Storage heater circuits

Storage heaters require a separate circuit for each heater. This is because, unlike direct acting heaters which are switched on and off as required, storage heaters are all switched on together during the 8-hour period. They cannot therefore be supplied from a ring circuit which is based on diversity of use of various appliances; each heater must have its own circuit.

The circuit for a storage radiator consists of 2.5 mm² 2-core and earth PVC sheathed cable. The cable starts at a 20 A fuseway in the time-controlled consumer unit and terminates at a 20 A double-pole switch fixed next to the storage radiator and connected to it with 3-core flexible cord via the cord outlet of the 20 A switch.

There are circumstances where two storage heaters are supplied from a single 30 A circuit. Each heater must then be supplied through a fused outlet which is a switched 13 A fused connection unit. Such an arrangement would be limited to two heaters

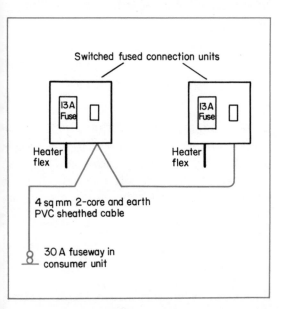

Two electric storage radiators, each having a loading not in excess of 3000 W may be supplied from one 30 A circuit each heater being supplied via a fused connection unit

having loadings of not more than 3 kW to prevent possible overheating of the fused connection unit.

Storage fan heater circuits

The circuits supplying the heater will be the same as those supplying storage radiators, but it is also necessary to provide a circuit for the fan.

As a fan takes very little current, small size cable as used for lighting circuits is suitable. The fan can, in fact, be supplied from a lighting circuit but rather than introduce a lighting circuit into a heating circuit it is better to feed the fan from a fused spur cable off the ring circuit (see Chapter 5). Where there is more than one storage fan heater all fans can be served by the one fused spur.

Switched outlet at heater

Both the heater and the fan require an isolating switch fixed near the heater to terminate the circuit cables and as a flex connection for the heater unit. As this heater will be supplied by two circuits, regulations require that the two switches are mechanically linked so that one cannot be switched off without the other.

To meet these requirements there is available a 25 A twin switch with or without pilot lights and with two cord outlets; one marked 'Fan' the other marked 'Heater'.

Automatic control

Heat output of a fan heater can be automatically controlled by introducing a room thermostat and/or timeswitch into the fan circuit, but generally it is sufficient to control the fan manually.

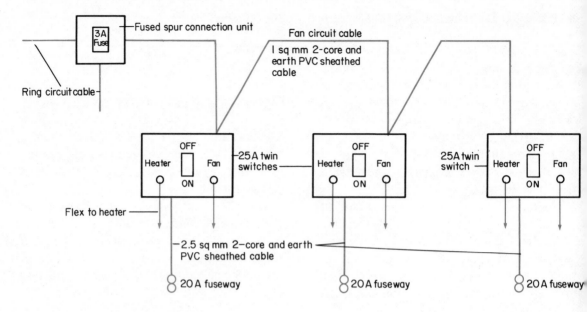

Fused spur connection unit

Ring circuit cable

Fan circuit cable

1 sq mm 2-core and earth PVC sheathed cable

OFF

Heater — Fan

ON

25 A twin switches

25A twin switch

Flex to heater

2.5 sq mm 2-core and earth PVC sheathed cable

20 A fuseway   20 A fuseway   20 A fuseway

The two circuits (heater and fan) needed for storage fan heaters. A separate circuit is supplying each heater but one circuit supplies all the fans

The two circuits of a storage fan heater terminate at a 25 A twin switch so that the supply to both is cut off simultaneously. Each has a separate 3-core flexible cord

2.5 sq mm 2-core and earth PVC sheathed cable

1.0 sq mm 2-core and earth PVC sheathed cable

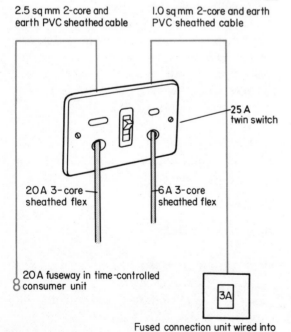

25 A twin switch

20 A 3-core sheathed flex

6 A 3-core sheathed flex

20 A fuseway in time-controlled consumer unit

3A

Fused connection unit wired into a ring circuit

Floor warming

Electrically warmed floors are applicable only to new houses, bungalows and flats during construction. If you move into a dwelling where this type of heating is installed, seek advice from the electricity board particularly regarding off-peak tariffs and running costs.

Electricaire heating

This is a system which directs warm air through a ducts system. It must be installed as a house is being built or being reconstructed under a home improvement scheme. The system needs a 45 A circuit from a 45 A fuseway to a control unit fixed near the unit.

Centrelec

This system is comparatively new. Before embarking on an installation it is advisable to discuss the project with the electricity board.

Chapter 9
Outdoor electrical extensions

Lighting and power to a detached garage, greenhouse or shed has to be a separate circuit running from the mains switchgear and not as an extension from one of the circuits in the house. Preferably, it is controlled by a separate main switch in the house which can be fed from the main consumer unit via an appropriate fuseway.

Flexible cord extensions

All too often a light in the shed or other outhouse is supplied from a flexible cord plugged into a socket-outlet in the kitchen and left as a 'permanent' extension, where it is likely to become damaged and be a shock hazard.

There are strict regulations concerning outdoor cables and wiring and the only recognised temporary supply is an extension lead. This may be with or without a reel and supplying a portable power tool, a portable light or a gardening tool, such as mower or hedgetrimmer, *only* during the time the appliance is actually being used.

The outdoor cable

The cable running from the house to the detached building, whether a mere shed or a fully-automatic greenhouse, can either be run overhead, buried in the ground, or run along a wall. Under no circumstances may it be fixed to a garden fence — for obvious reasons.

Overhead method

Ordinary PVC sheathed house wiring cable can be used as an outdoor overhead cable but it must be fixed at a height of at least 3.5 m (12 ft) above ground level. If the span between the house and outbuilding exceeds 3.5 m the cable must be supported by a catenary wire. This is a galvanised steel wire or cable secured by eyehooks to take the weight of a cable attached to it by clips or slings.

Provided you can get the height at the shed or garage, overhead wiring is satisfactory for short spans where, for instance, the shed (or garage) is at the side or back of the house within a few feet of the house. An alternative is an unjointed length of heavy gauge galvanised steel conduit or rigid conduit which will not fracture at sub-zero temperatures (below −5°C) this having the advantage that it may be at a height of 3 m (10 ft).

For long spans, which may require intermediate supporting poles an overhead cable is not an attractive proposition. It is often unsightly and is exposed to strong winds and other hazards.

Burying the cable underground

The underground method has the advantage that once installed it is permanent, out of sight and protected from the weather. To instal the cable, means digging a trench from the point where the cable enters the house to a corresponding point at the outbuilding. The trench has to be at least 500 m (18 in) deep and if it is to go through a vegetable plot where deep digging is likely, the depth should be increased in this section.

The route for the cable must be carefully selected. Concrete paths and terraces should be avoided and diversions made around obstacles. A good route for the cable is at

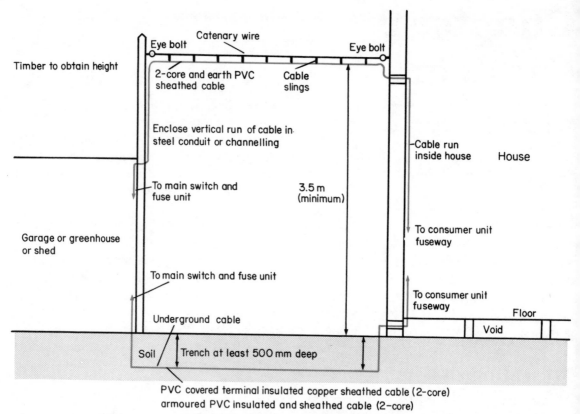

Eye bolt
Catenary wire
Eye bolt

Timber to obtain height

2-core and earth PVC sheathed cable

Cable slings

Enclose vertical run of cable in steel conduit or channelling

Cable run inside house   House

To main switch and fuse unit

3.5 m (minimum)

To consumer unit fuseway

Garage or greenhouse or shed

To main switch and fuse unit

To consumer unit fuseway

Floor

Underground cable

Void

Soil   Trench at least 500 mm deep

PVC covered terminal insulated copper sheathed cable (2-core) armoured PVC insulated and sheathed cable (2-core)

The outdoor cable supplying an outbuilding may be run overhead or underground. Both methods are shown here together with the cable routes

the edge of a border or lawn where the ground is least likely to be disturbed and digging the trench is usually easier. It is best to avoid taking the trench across a lawn for, unless the lawn is being renovated, the trench scar will remain.

Cables for outdoor use

Two types of cable are especially suited to running underground. One is PVC covered 2-core mineral-insulated copper-sheathed which is often referred to as MICC. The second type is PVC-covered armoured PVC-insulated and sheathed 2-core cable.

Ordinary PVC sheathed house wiring 2-core and earth cable can be run underground provided it is enclosed in heavy gauge galvanised steel conduit or rigid plastic conduit.

Fixing MICC cables

This cable with its distinctive orange PVC covering (also available in white PVC for indoor situations) is of small cross-sectional area — about that of a pencil — and can readily be continued in the section above ground. This type of cable can even be passed through an air vent into the void below the suspended floor of a dwelling or through a hole drilled in the wall above skirting level where the floor is solid or there is no access under the floor. Being very robust, the cable can be passed through a hole drilled in the door frame or sill, if it is not possible to drill a hole through the outside wall.

One possible snag with MICC cable is that the mineral insulation is hygroscopic and the prepared ends, as the sheath is stripped off, must be immediately fitted with seals to exclude moisture. The seals are fairly easy to fit, but instead of buying the special tools and materials needed for sealing, it is better to buy the cable with the seals fitted. In this case it is important that the required length has been accurately measured as a joint cannot be made in the buried section.

For some switchgear with screwed conduit entry holes, it is also necessary to have screwed glands on the ends of the MICC cable. These glands are fitted at the same time as the seals and are specified when buying the cable.

Earthing with MICC cable

The copper sheath of MICC cable is used as the earth-continuity conductor and because of this the junctions at the ends of the cable must be electrically sound so that continuity is maintained.

This continuity is provided by the screwed gland, or if there is no gland, by the seal which must be secured in the junction box fitted with MICC outlets. Seals are also available fitted with an earth screw for an earth conductor.

Fixing armoured PVC cable

This cable has much larger cross-sectional area than the MICC type, and as PVC insulation is not moisture absorbing the ends do not require seals. However, a gland is fitted to each end of this type of cable for screwing into a box or switchgear and to provide earth continuity; the wire armour being the earth conductor.

Glands are of the compression type and are similar to those of tees and elbows fitted to copper water pipes. They are easy to fit and need only a wrench and pliers.

Fixing the house section of cable

The outdoor cable whether MICC or armoured PVC can be run through the house in the conventional manner to the main switch position near the meter. Alternatively, the outdoor cable can be terminated at a junction box fixed to timber under the floor in close proximity to the point where the cable enters the house. From this box, ordinary PVC sheathed cable runs to the main switch.

When PVC sheathed cable is used in the outdoor section, either overhead or underground in conduit, it is continued (without conduit) to the mains without the necessity of a junction box.

Outbuildings

The whole of an installation in an outbuilding has to be under the control of an isolating double-pole switch so that the installation can be isolated from the mains at the turn of a switch when necessary. This switch is usually part of a switch fuse unit or the main switch of a consumer unit where there is more than one circuit.

In the outbuilding, the main switch whether a switch fuse unit or a consumer unit, is usually fixed in close proximity to the point where the incoming cable enters. This will reduce the length of run of the special cable.

The cable trench

Digging a trench for the cable is about the hardest part of the project. Before laying the cable, remove sharp stones and flints from the bottom of the trench and from the soil as it is replaced. If this is not done the PVC covering of the cable will be damaged and the copper sheath or wire armour become corroded.

66

Intermediate junction box

When fitting a junction box inside the house to join the MICC (or armoured) cable to the PVC sheathed cable running to the main switchgear this can be fixed to or between joists under the floorboards.

Where the floor is solid and the outside cable passes into the house above skirting level, fit the junction box to the inside wall. If preferred, the box can be sunk into the wall and have a moulded plastic cover to match the plate switches and socket-outlets in the room.

Connections to the switchfuse

Fix the switchfuse unit next to the main consumer unit and connect the incoming cable to the load terminals of the unit. If there is a spare fuseway connect a cable (of the same size as the outdoor circuit cable)

The outdoor special cable may be terminated in the house at a junction box and from this box ordinary PVC sheathed cable is run to the main switch and fuse unit

to the mains terminals of the switchfuse unit, and the other end to the fuseway of the consumer unit.

The fuse unit for the spare fuseway will be of the same rating as the circuit which is either 20 A or 30 A.

If there is no spare fuseway, the switch-fuse unit is connected to the mains by the electricity board. A pair of sheathed cables must be connected to the main terminals of the unit for the Board to connect to the meter.

Wiring in outbuildings or greenhouses

First connect the incoming cable to the switchfuse unit mounted on the wall at the appropriate height — 600 mm (2 ft) or more above the floor. This cable is connected to the mains terminals of the switch-fuse unit.

The circuit wiring is connected to the 'Load' terminals of this unit.

The wiring and the number of lights and socket-outlets in the outbuilding will depend

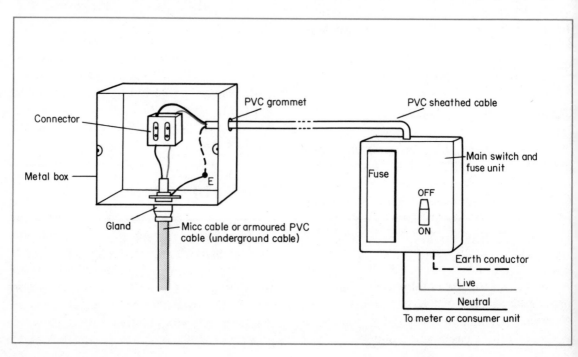

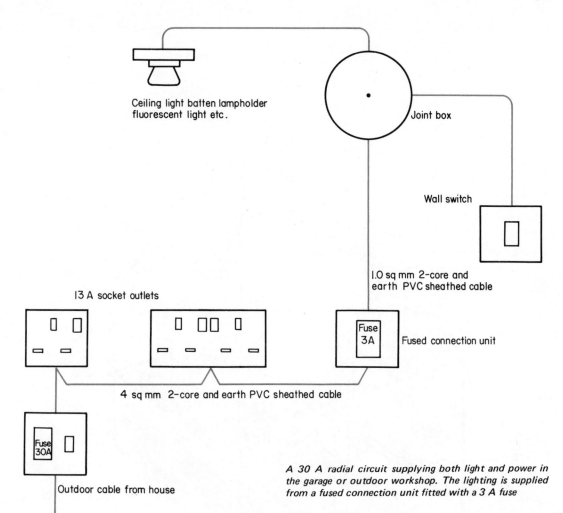

Ceiling light batten lampholder
fluorescent light etc.

Joint box

Wall switch

1.0 sq mm 2-core and
earth PVC sheathed cable

13 A socket outlets

Fuse
3A

Fused connection unit

4 sq mm 2-core and earth PVC sheathed cable

Fuse
30A

Outdoor cable from house

A 30 A radial circuit supplying both light and power in the garage or outdoor workshop. The lighting is supplied from a fused connection unit fitted with a 3 A fuse

on individual requirements, these depending on the function of the building. A shed may need only one light, but if used as a workshop it will need socket-outlets as well. A garage or greenhouse will need more socket-outlets which again will depend on the equipment used or installed.

For a greenhouse a number of socket-outlets, in addition to lighting, will be needed. These socket-outlets are usually mounted on a special distribution panel along with fused connection units and a main switch or a circuit breaker. As it is essential that heating is not switched off inadvertently, the socket-outlets and fused connection units should have neon indica-

tors. The fused connection units supply fixed heating, soil warming and can also supply the fixed lighting.

Wiring accessories and lighting fittings

Switches, socket-outlets and other accessories in the shed, garage or greenhouse can be of moulded plastic which is the same type as installed in the home. Where there is any risk of damaging them, metalclad switches and socket-outlets are installed. In the greenhouse, protection from water spray is desirable.

Batten lampholders, close ceiling fittings

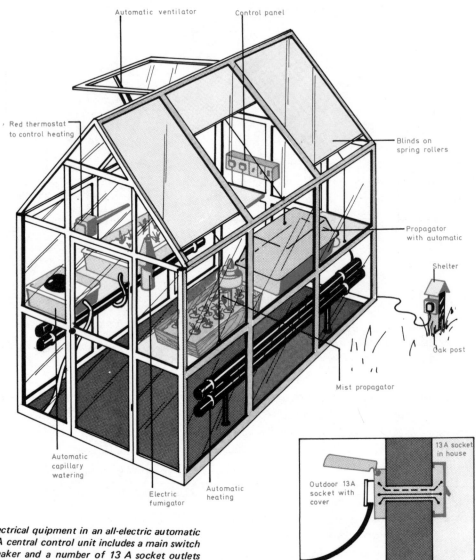

Automatic ventilator

Control panel

Red thermostat
to control heating

Blinds on
spring rollers

Propagator
with automatic

Shelter

Oak post

Mist propagator

Automatic
capillary
watering

Electric
fumigator

Automatic
heating

13 A socket
in house

Outdoor 13A
socket with
cover

*Layout of electrical quipment in an all-electric automatic
greenhouse. A central control unit includes a main switch
or circuit breaker and a number of 13 A socket outlets
for portable appliances and fused connection units for
fixed wiring*
*Socket outlets installed outdoors can either be fixed to
the house wall or to posts protected by weatherproof
covers. Ordinary socket outlets can be fitted with weatherproof covers as shown*

and other non-pendant lighting fittings, including fluorescent, are used in these situations. If a fitting is to be installed out of doors it must be of the weatherproof type.

Weatherproof lighting fittings are available in an extensive range of attractive designs giving a wide choice to the householder. These include bulkhead totally-enclosed all-insulated fittings for fluorescent or tungsten lamps.

Number of circuits

Only rarely will more than one circuit be needed in an outbuilding. For most outbuildings, this can be a 30 A radial circuit which may serve up to a total of five 13 A socket-outlets plus a fused connection unit for the fixed lighting. Portable lights can be run off a plug and socket.

The fused connection unit is fitted with a 3 A fuse and the lighting section of the circuit can then be wired in the small-size cable used for lighting circuits. This is 1.0 mm² 2-core and earth PVC sheathed. Where only one 13 A socket and lighting is required, such as in the small workshop, the circuit can be 20 A wired in 2.5 mm² cable instead of 4 mm² cable used in a 30 A circuit.

Mains cable rating

The cable from the house must be of 30 A rating (4 mm²) where the internal circuit is 30 A. Where the circuit in the outbuilding is only 20 A, the cable from the house need be only of 20 A rating (2.5 mm²).

Running a cable underground out-of-doors is a difficult job and it is always as well to use the 4 mm² cable to allow for future extensions. The larger size costs very little more than 2.5 mm².

Outdoor socket-outlets

There are many occasions when outdoor socket-outlets come in useful, for example, for supplying an electric mower, a hedge-cutter, a power tool and other electric tools. Socket-outlets are also necessary for pool lighting, a garden fountain operated by an electric pump and garden lighting. These latter can be from either mains voltage or low voltage via a transformer.

Outdoor socket-outlets are of the weatherproof type or are fitted with weatherproof covers. They are best supplied by MICC cable buried in the ground in the same way as a cable feeding an outbuilding. Socket-outlets can be fixed to posts in the garden or to a garden wall. They should be served by a separate circuit from the house consumer unit with a switch installed in a convenient position for switching off from the house. This switch can be a high sensitivity earth-leakage circuit-breaker to give a person using the garden tools and equipment additional protection from electric shock. (See Chapter 1 for information on earth-leakage circuit-breakers).

In wet weather it is possible that the earth-leakage circuit-breaker will trip. This will happen if a hedgecutter is used when the hedge is wet and for this reason, it is a good protection. A high-sensitivity earth-leakage circuit-breaker should not be installed in a greenhouse, where there is a risk of it tripping. This may ruin the growing crops in soil warming beds and propagators.

Chapter 10
Electrical hardware

The 'hardware' of home wiring includes switches, ceiling roses, lampholders, socket-outlets, fused connection units (fused spur units); joint boxes; consumer units, fuse-boards and main switch and fuse units or switchfuse units.

These are mainly of moulded plastic in white (of various tones), brown, or in various colours. Some accessories may be made of metal instead of moulded plastic.

Styling and quality

With the possible exception of joint boxes, all this hardware is exposed to view and, because of this, styling has been an important factor in the design. An important factor of home decor is the question of matching accessories. Switches, socket-outlets and fused connection units are available in patterns to match as well as in colour tone. The colour may also extend to ceiling roses, lampholders, batten lamp-holders and ceiling switches which also have the overall matching appearance. Joint boxes are often under the floorboards or in the roof space but these have good styling which can be an asset where surface-mounted and exposed to view.

Quality of hardware is generally high, but low quality accessories are also available — not necessarily at low prices.

The various accessories are dealt with in the respective sections of this book. In this section they are covered in more detail so that the reader may have some guidance as to the correct type to select for a specific purpose.

Current rating of switches

Switches used in the home are: 5 A lighting switches, 20 A switches for controlling storage heaters, water heaters and other appliances; and 30-60 A switches for controlling cookers and other heavy current consuming appliances.

A selection of switches for lighting and power are shown below and on the opposite page. These are all double pole switches of 20 A and above

20 A double-pole switch with neon indicator

20 A double-pole switch with flex outlet

30–50 A double-pole switch

Metal clad 20 A double-pole switch with neon indicator

Lighting switches

The one-way switch

The conventional modern lighting switch is the single-pole one-way on/off plate switch. This is a small-gap (not quite micro-gap though often referred to as such) switch mounted behind a moulded plastic 'square' faceplate. The switch has a rocker or a dolly to operate it; the dolly now largely superseded by the rocker switch. The switch can be mounted on either a surface plastic box, or on a flush metal box as desired.

The 2-way switch

The 2-way plateswitch is identical in size and appearance to the one-way switch but has a 2-way action and has three terminals instead of two, which are necessary for the circuit wiring. Its function is to enable a light to be switched on and off from two positions.

The intermediate switch

The intermediate plateswitch is also of identical size and appearance to the one-way switch. It has double action like the 2-way switch and has four terminals. Its function is to enable a light to be switched on or off from three (or more according to the number of intermediate switches in the circuit) positions in conjunction with two 2-way switches.

Multi-gang switches

A multi-gang switch consists of two or more switches on the one switchplate. A square faceplate similar to a one-way switch is made in 2- and 3-gang versions. Where 4- to 6-gang switch units are needed; these are incorporated on a rectangular (double) switchplate.

The two (or three) switches of a multigang square plate assembly, and often installed in the home, are all 2-way switches; though, in fact, one or more are used for the one-way control of the lights. The reason for this is a production one. When used as a one-way switch, only two of the terminals of each switch are used, the third remaining blank. In fact, any 2-way switch can be used either as a 1-way or a 2-way switch.

Intermediate switches are made only in single/switch assemblies.

Round switches

Until the introduction of the plateswitch, the lighting switch was a circular switch and had a tumbler action instead of the small gap contact action. These switches are still in service in very many houses. They are mainly surface mounted, either on hardwood blocks or more latterly on plastic pattresses.

Tumbler switches are also made in a flush mounting version. This is a coverless switch fixed inside a hardwood box and covered by a metal plate, secured to the switch by a centrally positioned screwed ring. Plastic plate versions are also available.

The 20 A switch

The 20 A switch is a double-pole unit for the remote switching or isolating of fixed electrical appliances. It should be situated near the appliance and connected to it with either flexible cord or fixed cable.

The switch is made in switchplate form having the same size square plate as the lighting switch. As the switch unit is larger, it requires a deeper box than the plaster depth or shallow box used for a lighting plateswitch. It is available with or without neon indicator, and with or without cord outlet. For immersion heaters and water heaters switches are available with the plate engraved in red – WATER HEATER.

As a plateswitch it can be mounted on a surface plastic box or a metal flush box. Alternative versions are designed as surface-mounted units, either with a composite box or for mounting on a pattress.

The 30-60 A switch

This switch is a plateswitch for either surface or flush mounting. It is available with or without a neon indicator and is made in a number of current ratings: 30 A; 45-50 A and 60 A.

The 30 A size is used largely as an isolation switch for instantaneous water heaters, and the two larger sizes are used as cooker control switches in place of the conventional cooker control unit incorporating a socket-outlet for an electric kettle (see Chapter 6).

The cooker control versions are available with the word COOKER engraved in red letters.

A cord operated ceiling switch. These are used mainly in bathrooms and as an extra switch in the bedroom above the bedhead. The ceiling switch illustrated has an integral backplate and matches the modern loop in ceiling rose of the same make.

Cord-operated switches

The cord-operated switch is used principally as a ceiling-mounted switch for installation in bathrooms in place of the conventional wall switch, where the wall switch would be within reach of a person using the bath or shower. As a lighting switch it is also used as a bedhead switch either in conjunction with the wall switch on a 2-way circuit, or to switch the bedhead light on and off. One version of the switch is suitable for wall as well as for ceiling mounting.

Cord-operated ceiling switches for controlling heaters and other appliances are available in 15 A current rating, in a number of versions: single-pole, double-pole, and double-pole with pilot light.

The 30 A ceiling switch

The 30 A double-pole cord-operated ceiling switch is of recent introduction. It has been designed for controlling a 5-7 kW instantaneous water heater supplying shower units installed in bathrooms or in other positions where a wall switch would be within reach of a person using the shower (or bath).

Ceiling roses

The modern ceiling rose is a plastic backplate containing three terminal blocks situated in-line, an earthing terminal and an optional strain terminal for the connection of a strain cable in the flex which supports a heavy shade. The backplate has 'knockout' facilities for sheathed cables and a screw-on cover with an outlet for the pendant flexible cord.

A built-in safety feature of this ceiling rose is the shielding of the live conductor terminal block. This is now a regulation requirement designed to prevent a person, when re-flexing a pendant fitting and not

Ceiling roses. The top photograph showing the cover removed and the lower picture shows a plug-in ceiling rose which makes connecting the cord simple

having taken the elementary precaution of switching off at the mains, accidentally touching the live terminal and receiving a fatal shock. In the latest designs the other two terminal blocks (the neutral and switch return wire terminal block) are also shielded, although this is not a regulation requirement.

Loop-in facilities

The central live terminal block and one end terminal block are the live and neutral terminal blocks for the looping in terminal connections of the mains cable. Because of this the ceiling rose is called a loop-in ceiling rose.

As shown in the illustration, the loop-in ceiling rose also functions as a joint box so obviating the need for joint boxes in the circuit. With its integral backplate the ceiling rose is fixed direct to the ceiling; no intervening pattress or block being required.

Old type ceiling roses

The old type ceiling rose, either of porcelain or plastic, is still in service in many homes. It is usually mounted on either a hardwood block or a plastic pattress. There are two principal versions: the 2-plate type, which is a ceiling rose having two terminals; and the 3-plate type which has three terminals, the third being for looping in the live feed of the circuits. This latter terminal has the same purpose as the live terminal of the modern loop-in ceiling rose but, in this case, the terminal is unshielded and not marked as 'live'.

Pattresses on which ceiling roses are mounted, sometimes include a terminal where the earth conductor can be connected. Another pattern has two terminals, one of which can be for the live loop-in with a 2-plate ceiling rose.

When re-flexing these old ceiling roses or, when intending to replace them with up-to-

date patterns, a careful examination of the connections is advised.

Plug-in ceiling roses

These are special ceiling roses having socket connections for the circuit wires and a small plug to which the pendant flex is attached and plugged into the socket section. A screw cover encloses the socket and plug and the unit resembles a conventional ceiling rose.

It has the advantage that it can be detached for cleaning or interchanged with other plain pendants without disturbing the fixed wiring.

Detachable ceiling plate

This unit is of metal in two sections, one fixed and containing the circuit wire terminals, the other attached to the pendant is detachable from the fixed base by a sliding action. The pendant can be a flex, a rod fitting, or a hook and chain pendant.

Multi-light pendants and other special pendant fittings have a conventional fixed ceiling plate in a variety of shapes and diameters.

Lampholders

The majority of pendant lampholders are of moulded plastic and of BC (Bayonet Cap) pattern for use with the ordinary electric light bulb. These lampholders have cord grips for use with flexible cord plain pendants but are threaded for fixing direct to wall lights and pendant fittings (other than plain pendants).

A switched version is used in table lamps and floor standards.

Another version is the SBC (small bayonet cap) lampholder used with SBC candle lamps of the plain and twisted patterns.

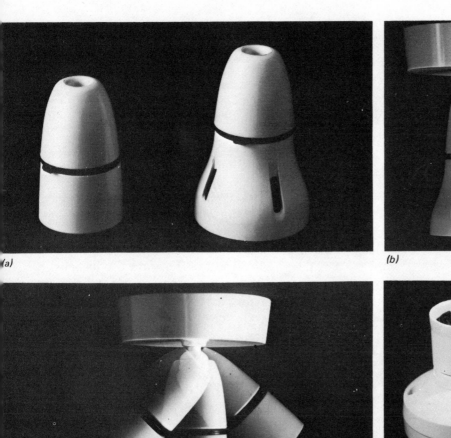

(a)

(b)

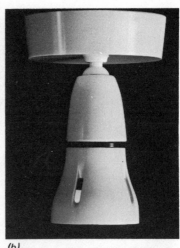

(c)

(d)

(a) Short skirt lampholder. (b) Deep skirt lampholder

(c) Angle batten lampholder. (d) Table lamp dimmer

Earthed lampholders

Metal lampholders have to be earthed as do some heat-resisting lampholders where the metal lamp cap holder is separated from the plastic. 3-core flex is used with these lampholders.

ES lampholders

The ES lampholder has a large size thread to accept the Edison Screw (ES) lamp cap of continental and American bulbs. It also has a centre contact corresponding with

the centre contact of the ES bulb. When wiring these lampholders, it is essential that the neutral wire is connected to the lamp cap terminal and that the live wire is connected to the centre contact terminal.

GES lampholders

These GES (Goliath Edison Screw) lampholders are used for jumbo size bulbs which are rarely used in the home. In contrast the MES (Miniature Edison Screw) bulb is the common torch bulb and the lamp cap of fairy light bulbs.

Joint boxes
(a) 4-terminal joint box used for lighting circuits

(b) 30 A ring circuit joint box having separate
terminals for single-strand cables

(c) Universal joint box

SBC lampholders

The SBC (Small Bayonet Cap) lampholder is fitted to wall lights and to multi-light pendants for candle lamps and other special bulbs having an SBC cap.

Batten lampholders

Originally designed for light battens on the theatre stage, these are really low-priced complete lighting fittings for use where there is limited headroom and in other confined spaces. They are also installed in bathrooms, WC's and in kitchens as an alternative to a pendant fitting (see page 103).

Skirted batten lampholders

When fitted in the bathroom and in similar situations, the batten lampholder (or any lampholder) should have a deep HO (Home Office) pattern skirt. This is to prevent a person, when changing a bulb, touching the metal clamp while the bulb is making contact with the live pins of the lampholder.

Modern designs of batten lampholders have loop-in facilities and are versions of the loop-in ceiling roses. Heat-resisting types are available which, in many situations, are essential to prevent overheating of the lampholder and wiring.

Joint boxes

Joint boxes are usually circular and form part of the circuit wiring. They are fixed permanently to the house structure and used principally in lighting circuits. Joint boxes are available in 4- 5- and 6-terminal versions.

A 3-terminal joint box of 30 A current rating is used for ring circuits to connect spur cables to the ring cable, as shown in the illustration.

Socket-outlets

The socket-outlet is the fixed portion of a plug and socket arrangement and the termination point of circuit wiring to provide a ready means of connecting portable appliances to the fixed mains wiring.

The 13 A socket-outlet for use with the flat-pin fused plug is the standard socket in Britain for domestic installations. It is made in many variants: single switched socket, single non-switched socket; double socket, switched and non-switched, and switched with neon indicator. All these versions are available in the plate type for mounting on surface and flush boxes.

The single socket is mounted on a 1-gang box; the double on a 2-gang box, and two singles may be mounted side by side on a dual box. This dual box is slightly wider than the double or 2-gang box and has extra screw lugs for the separate sockets.

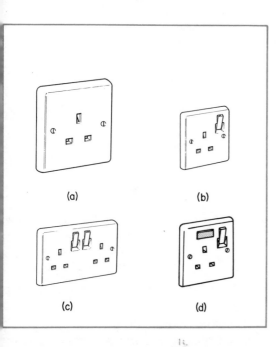

(a)   (b)

(c)   (d)

13 A socket-outlets. (a) Unswitched 13 A socket-outlet (b) Switched 13 A socket-outlet (c) Switched double 13 A socket-outlet (d) Switched 13 A socket-outlet with neon indicator

Surface pattern socket-outlets are designed only for surface mounting and are usually mounted on a pattress.

Fused round pin plugs

Although the fused plug is associated with the 13 A flat pin plug and socket of the ring circuit, fused round pin plugs are made to the appropriate British Standard (BS 546) and may be found in some homes. The fuses are of the cartridge type but slightly smaller than the 13 A plug fuse. The ratings and colours are: 5 A (red); 2 A (yellow) and 1 A (green), made to BS 646.

These fuses are fitted in some clock connectors, so if the clock connector has either a 2 A or a 1 A fuse, check whether it is stamped BS 642. If it is, buy the same size replacements and not a 2 A (black) or 3 A (red) which are for 13 A plugs.

Fused connection units

A fused connection unit (originally known as a fused spur box) provides a fused outlet in a ring circuit as an alternative to a fused plug and socket-outlet (see Chapter 5). It is used to supply fixed appliances and remotely positioned fixed lighting.

The fuses are cartridge fuses of the same size, colours and current ratings as used with the 13 A fused plug.

Proposed 16 A plug

An entirely new plug and socket outlet having a current rating of 16 A is being developed world-wide and will replace all existing plugs and sockets including the 13 A fused plug and the round pin plugs used in the UK. It is unlikely to be in production before 1980 and it will be many years after this before existing plugs and sockets are entirely obsolete.

It is also expected that the 13 A ring circuit sockets will be able to be replaced without modification to existing wiring.

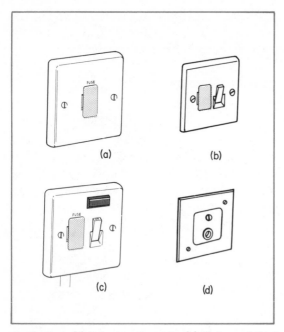

A selection of fused connection units. (a) 13 A unswitched fused connection unit (b) 13 A switched fused connection unit (c) 13 A switched fused connection unit with neon indicator and flex outlet (d) Fused clock connector

The sockets will probably be twin units for mounting on a one-gang box, but for the ring circuit the twin unit will consist of one socket and a fused unit.

Fused clock connectors

A fused clock connector is a small non-switched fused outlet designed expressly for supplying a mains electric clock.

The unit is in two sections: a fixed base which is connected to the fixed circuit wiring, and another section in the form of a flat pin plug which plugs into sockets in the base. The plug section carries the flex of the clock and contains the fuse. The plug is secured in the base by a retaining screw. This prevents the plug being pulled out accidentally and stopping the clock.

Fused clock connectors are sometimes used for other appliances, such as extractor fans.

Full details on wiring electric clocks are given in Chapter 5.

Shaver supply units and shaver sockets

The shaver supply unit is designed especially for shavers used in the bathroom. It has a 2-pin socket which accepts British, Continental and American standard 2-pin round and flat pin plugs.

The unit contains a transformer to isolate the socket from the earthed mains supply to provide greater safety in the bathroom. The voltage at the socket is 240 V, but a dual version provides an alternative voltage of 110 V for American shavers.

A thermal cut-out in the unit prevents any mains voltage portable appliance (or portable lamp) other than a shaver being plugged into the unit and used in the bathroom.

A shaver socket is a socket which accepts the 2-pin plugs of shavers but does not contain a transformer. It is therefore cheaper and may be installed in any room except a bathroom. Some models are fitted with thermal cut-out.

Some striplights intended for shaving mirror lighting are fitted with a shaver socket. Some have an isolating transformer and may be installed in the bathroom. Others are simply shaver sockets with no transformer. These may be installed anywhere except in the bathroom.

Cord outlet units

A cord outlet is simply a moulded plastic 'square' plate containing three terminals and a cord grip behind the plate and a flexible cord entry hole in the centre. It is mounted on the standard flush or surface socket outlet box.

The function of the unit is to provide a connection of an appliance to the circuit wiring other than by socket-outlet or fused connection unit. It is installed in situations, such as in a bathroom, to connect the flex of towel rails and other heaters where the switched outlet must be out of reach of a person using the bathroom. In these situations the switch is usually a cord-operated ceiling switch.

Socket multi-adaptors

These are also known as plug adaptors. They are inserted into socket-outlets to enable more than one plug to be used from any one socket-outlet. The two outlet 13 A unit is commonplace, since it enables an extra plug to be used from a 13 A socket-outlet.

Other versions have mixed ratings for 5 A and 2 A plugs; the adaptor in these containing a fuse to protect the smaller outlets. Some makes have no fuse, although designed for plugs of various current ratings. These adaptors are unauthorised and should not be used in the home. Also available are shaver socket adaptors enabling a shaver to be used from a 13 A socket-outlet.

Outdoor wiring accessories

Socket-outlets, switches and other wiring accessories exposed to rain and snow outside the house must be weatherproof. These are either metalclad or are unbreakable types in plastic or rubber. Accessories which are installed outside, but under cover, can be of the plastic-moulded type.

Accessories installed in the garage, garden shed or greenhouse are normally of the plastic-moulded type.

Consumer units and switchgear

Consumer units situated at the mains for supplying have already been covered in Chapters 3 and 5. As previously explained these replace the old-fashioned main switch and fuse units and have also largely replaced the fuseboard with its separate main switch and fuse unit.

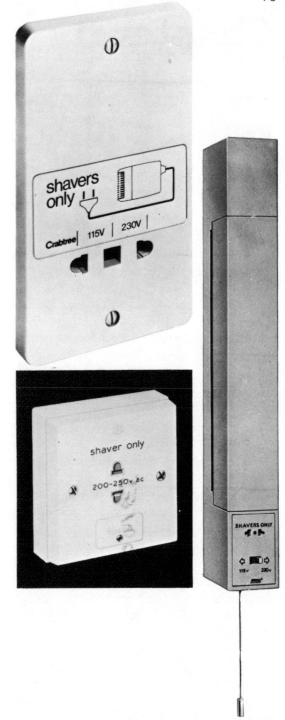

Shaver sockets. The top illustration shows a shaver supply unit for installation in bathrooms and the bottom picture illustrates a shaver socket for use in rooms other than bathrooms. A shaver mirror light with shaver socket suitable for installation in bathrooms is shown on the right

Chapter 11
Electrical repairs about the home

There are many electrical repair jobs which the householder can do himself, such as mending fuses, replacing flex, fitting a new plug, etc.

It is essential to have a card of the different sizes of fuse wire and/or spare cartridge fuses for each of the current ratings of the circuit fuses.

What to do when a fuse blows

First find out which fuse has blown. Is it a lighting circuit, a ring circuit, water heater circuit or any other circuit?

If you have a modern consumer unit (or fuseboard) having fuses which are colour coded you will know that for a lighting circuit you will have to check the white fuses and, if a ring circuit fuse, or a cooker circuit fuse, it will be red. If the immersion heater circuit fuse has blown the fuse colour will be either blue or yellow, see Table 2 on page 11.

Details of the circuits should be available at the consumer unit or fuseboard. The consumer unit usually has a sticker on the fuse cover where circuit details are listed. This enables you to know which fuse has blown. Check the circuit number with the list and withdraw the appropriate fuse holder.

If the consumer unit has no circuit list, or there is a number of main switch and fuse units, self-adhesive labels can be used. These should not be stuck to the actual fuse holder, for if you remove more than one fuse holder of the same current rating, you may mix them up.

In general, a ground floor lighting circuit will include the lighting points on the ground floor and the first floor circuit will serve the lighting points on the first floor. However, there are sometimes a number of lights which do not follow this rule and some may be fed from the ring circuits. The same can apply to the ring circuits with some socket-outlets on the ground floor being connected to the first floor ring circuit and some may possibly be served by one or more radial circuits, see Chapter 5. It is an advantage to check all lights and socket-outlets and list them, so that when a fuse blows you will know exactly what are affected.

Turning off the main switch

It is always good practice to turn off the main switch when mending fuses. This is true even in the case of the modern consumer unit where the fuses have a separate cover and no live parts are exposed when taking off the cover or when removing a fuse.

Even if you don't switch off the main switch before taking out the fuse, you should switch off before you replace it in case there is a fault which will cause the fuse to blow immediately. In this case the fuse will 'blow' with a bang which can be frightening, but this is not dangerous with modern fuse holders which shield the fusewire.

A disadvantage of turning off the main switch is that all lights and power go off and mains electric clocks have to be reset after restoring the power. Always have a torch handy near the fuseboard or consumer unit.

Before mending a fuse try and find out why it blew. If it blew as you switched on a light it is probably the bulb. Some bulbs contain a fuse to prevent the circuit fuse blowing when the bulb fails. Examine the bulb and if this appears in good condition examine the light flex.

If a lighting circuit fuse blows apparently without warning, it is probable that the fuse wire has deteriorated. However, if the fuse is of the cartridge type, which does not deteriorate, the trouble is more serious. A ring circuit fuse blows if there is a fault in the circuit. It is rarely due to a faulty appliance, since in this case, the plug fuse blows leaving the circuit intact.

Mending a fuse

Remove the fuse cover from the consumer unit. Locate the blown fuse and withdraw the fuse holder. Examine the fuse element — fuse wire — and it will be obvious if it has blown. If the fuse is of the cartridge type

this has to be removed for testing as it is not possible to tell by visual inspection whether it has blown.

Rewirable fuses are mended as follows:

(i) Having removed the fuse holder from the consumer unit or fuse-board, loosen the two screws and take out the bits of fuse wire remaining.

(ii) Clean off any melted blobs of copper and clean off any burn marks.

(iii) Select the fuse wire of correct current rating on the fuse wire card.

(iv) Pass the end of the wire through the ceramic or asbestos tube and connect it to the terminal.

(v) Cut the wire to length and connect this end to the other terminal. If a clamp type terminal, place the wire end under the washer clockwise and when tightening the screw take care not to stretch the fuse wire. If stretched, its current rating will drop and overheating may result.

Mending a rewirable fuse

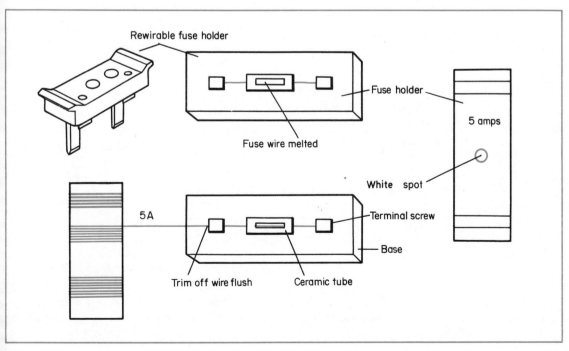

82

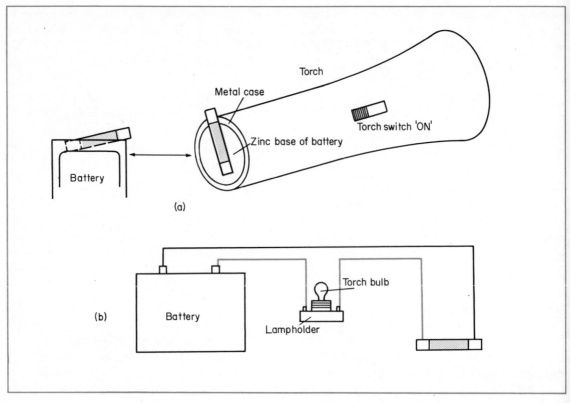

(a)

(b)

Testing a cartridge fuse. (a) The base of a metal torch is unscrewed and the fuse placed inside with one contact on the case, the other on the zinc base of the battery. If the torch lights when switched on the fuse is OK. (b) A bulb and battery as an alternative method

(vi) Trim off the ends of wire.

(vii) Turn off the main switch (if not already turned off) and insert the holder in the fuseway.

(viii) Turn on the main switch. If there is an immediate 'bang' the fuse has blown again indicating a serious fault. It is advisable in this case to have an electrician to locate the fault.

(ix) If the fuse is OK, test the lights. If you suspect the flex of a lighting fitting caused the fuse to blow, attend to this before turning on the room switch.

(x)   Finally replace the fuse cover.

The procedure for 'mending' a cartridge fuse is simple. It is replaced by another.

Remove the cartridge from its holder and lay it aside for testing. Select a fuse of the same current rating (and therefore the same colour and the same physical dimensions) fit it into the fuse holder and replace the fuse holder into the consumer unit. Switch on and, as with rewirable fuses, if the fuse immediately blows the fault is serious.

Miniature circuit breakers

If the consumer unit contains MCB's (miniature circuit breakers) instead of fuses the procedure when the lights fail is simple. Take a torch to the consumer unit and note which MCB is switched off; this is the faulty

A consumer unit fitted with mcbs (miniature circuit breakers). A typical mcb of the push-button type is shown below

circuit. Unless you think a flex is faulty or some other fault has caused the MCB to trip, you simply restore the switch to its 'ON' position. If it trips immediately, or you cannot switch it on, there is a circuit fault because it is not possible to close a circuit breaker against a fault.

There are various types of circuit breaker switch. Some are press-button, where the button pops out when the circuit breaker operates. With other types, the switch trips to a central position between ON and OFF so that it is obvious that it has tripped and was not switched off.

Earth-leakage circuit breakers

If the installation is protected by an ELCB (earth-leakage circuit breaker) this will normally be because there is no conventional effective earthing. The earth-leakage circuit breaker may protect the whole installation or only a portion, in which case there will be more than one.

The ELCB trips and cuts off the current when a live wire or connection comes into contact with earthed metal. Where there is conventional earthing the fuse will blow when this fault occurs, but where there is an ELCB instead, the fuse will not blow.

Before the current can be restored (the ELCB switched on) it is necessary to locate and repair the fault for, as with the MCB, an ELCB will not close when a fault remains. In this case a current flows through the earth conductor and the tripping coil of the circuit breaker. If you cannot rectify the fault immediately try and isolate the faulty section; this is easy if you suspect an appliance as you simply pull out the plug.

A disadvantage of having only a single

An example of a current operated ELCB (earth leakage circuit breaker) which is made in high sensitivity versions to provide personal protection

ELCB on an installation is that a single fault will cut off the current to the entire installation. It is therefore an advantage to have more than one ELCB but this is possible only where there is either more than one consumer unit or where individual circuits, such as the cooker circuit, are supplied from a separate main switch and fuse unit.

Renewing flexes

When a flexible cord shows signs of wear, or damaged, it must be replaced without delay. You need a new length of flex of the same type and size, see Table 6 on page 98.

The flex of a plain pendant is traditionally twisted twin, but circular sheathed flex is now used extensively. Where the existing flex is twisted twin, you should replace it

with circular sheathed at an early opportunity. This may also mean replacing the ceiling roses and lampholders, for many of the older types will not accept circular sheathed flex as the cord grips are designed for twisted twin flex.

The flex can be changed as follows:

(i)   Remove the old flex and cut the new flex to the same length.
(ii) Prepare the ends of the circular sheathed by stripping off about 100 mm (4 in) for the ceiling rose end and about 50 mm (2 in) of sheath for a lampholder.

You can now connect the flex to the ceiling rose but, if you have cut the new flex to the correct length, fit the lampholder first. This should be done on a bench or table instead of from the top of steps.

Wiring the lampholder and ceiling rose

The flex is connected to the lampholder as follows:

(i)   Unscrew the lampholder cap.
(ii) Strip about 12 mm (½ in) of insulation from the two wires.

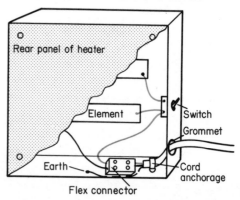

Connecting 3-core flex to an electric fire. Connect the brown wire of the flex to the L terminal, the blue to the N terminal and the green/yellow to the earth terminal. Make sure the sheath is secure under the anchorage and replace the access panel

(iii) Bend the bared ends double to provide a better grip in the terminals.

(iv) Loosen the terminal screws and insert the wires.

(v) Tighten the screws.

(vi) Thread on the lampholder cap and screw it on to the lampholder.

(vii) Check that the unsheathed portion does not protrude from the lampholder, if it does, disconnect the flex, shorten the wires and repeat the process.

Where a lampholder has an earth screw you use 3-core flex. The third core (green-yellow) is secured to this terminal which is usually of the clamp type. Do not double the end of this wire but place it under the clamp screw washer clockwise and tighten the screw.

To connect flex to the ceiling rose, first thread on the ceiling rose cover. This is often forgotten. Modern ceiling roses have post terminals, so prepare the ends of the two wires as for lampholder and insert them in the appropriate terminal holes and tighten the screws. When loosening the screws to do this, take care not to screw them out or you will have difficulty in replacing them from the top of a pair of steps. Place the insulated portion of the wires over the anchorage and screw on the cover.

Check that the unsheathed portion of the wires is contained within the ceiling rose. If not you will have to disconnect the flex, shorten the ends and repeat the process. If you are reflexing more than one pendant, and all ceiling roses and lampholders are identical, carefully measure the trimmed ends of the first and use this as a guide for the remainder.

If you are wiring the ceiling rose with 3-core flex because the lampholder has to be earthed, you connect the earth core to the earth terminal of the ceiling rose. Other-

wise the flex is not connected to the earth terminal; this being used only for the earth conductors of the circuit wiring.

Where you have the old-type ceiling roses and are not replacing them by the modern type, you will find that the method of connecting and anchoring the flex differs. Many ceiling roses have clamp-type terminals, but some have tunnel type. In some types, wires are anchored to slots or holes in the ceiling rose base, usually enabling sheathed flex to be used, but with others, the flex is gripped by tightening the cover, which will only accommodate twisted twin flex, or the insulated ends of sheathed flex from which the sheath is removed. The solution here is to fit modern ceiling roses.

Rewiring multi-light fittings

When it becomes necessary to renew the flex of a multi-light pendant fitting, or a single-light pendant, other than a plain pendant, it is rewired using the same type of flex, usually parallel twin flex. First remove the screws securing the ceiling plate to its box or pattress. Carefully lower the pendant a few inches to give you access to a porcelain or plastic block connector which joins the fitting wires to the circuit cable.

Loosen the screws securing the circuit wires so that you can remove the fitting with the connector attached to its flex, but make sure you don't disturb any jointed circuit wires. As a precaution you can bind them with adhesive tape, provided someone else can take the weight of the fitting while you bind the tape.

A multi-light fitting will have a flex to each lampholder, one core of all flexes being joined in one terminal of the connector, the other core of all flexes being joined in the other terminal. Rewire the fitting in this manner and you can then connect it to the circuit wires and refix the

86

pendant in the reverse order from taking it down.

A single light special fitting will have only one flex so it is best to leave the connector secured to the circuit wires with no risk of disturbing jointed conductors.

Earthing metal lighting fittings

An electric light fitting having exposed metalwork has to be earthed. To do this you connect a short length of green PVC insulated earth cable from the earth terminal of the pattress box to an earth terminal on the fitting, so obviating 3-core flex when wiring the fitting.

If, as is usual in an old installation, there is no earth at the lighting point and probably no earth terminal on the fitting, to earth the fitting means running an earth wire from the consumer unit especially for the fitting and then fixing a terminal screw to the fitting.

Reflexing portable appliances

When a portable appliance requires a new flex the most difficult job is usually locating the terminals to which the flex is connected. In many instances this means partly dismantling the appliance. In others it means simply removing a terminal cover, an example being the steam or dry thermostatically controlled electric iron. Other appliances, such as electric kettles, some coffee percolators, non-automatic irons and similar small appliances containing heating elements, incorporate a removable flex adaptor. Renewing a flex in these cases means fitting it to the adaptor and sometimes in replacing the adaptor by a new one.

Radiant electric fires, convectors, fan heaters and practically every electric heater

has its flex passing through a grommet into a terminal block situated within the casing. To get to the terminal block usually means removing a back or side panel or, in some cases, removing the panel under the base of the heater. With other models of heater, the whole of the front panel complete with the elements and reflectors, is removed to obtain access to the terminal block.

Having located the terminals you can disconnect the old flex, taking careful note of the polarity of the terminals. These may be marked for live and neutral or have splashes of red and black paint. If not, note very carefully the terminals with the red (or brown) wire and the black (or blue) wire. The earth terminal will be obvious as it is fixed to the metal frame of the heater. Before you can pull the disconnected flex out through the grommet you will have to release the cord anchorage, so note how this is effected for the new flex anchorage.

The new flex will normally be of the same type, size and length as the old but if you have any doubt that it is not the original flex and not the correct type make sure the new flex is correct. If the insulation of the wires within the heater has obviously been affected by the heat, the new flex must be heat resisting. The length of a portable heater flex should not be in excess of 2 m (6 ft) or 3 m (9 ft) including connections.

Pass the end of the new flex through the grommet and pull through sufficient flex for the connection at the terminal block and earth terminal. Strip off enough sheath to make the connection — no more. If braided flex, remove the braid to the required length and slip on a rubber sleeve to contain the ends of the braid and fillers. Strip sufficient insulation from the ends of the conductors for making the connection in the terminals. Tighten the terminal screws and secure the flex in the anchorage.

Replace the panel or panels or terminal

over as necessary. Fit the plug on the other end of the flex (see wiring a plug, later in this chapter) and test the heater by inserting the plug into its socket-outlet.

The procedure for fitting a flex to other appliances is similar, except for those appliances incorporating a flex adaptor (see below). The important thing to remember is to fit the right type and the right size of flex.

Fitting flex to a connector

A flex connector such as that fitted to an electric kettle is made in two principal forms though with many variants. The older pattern of connector which is still widely used is made in two halves which are split apart to connect the flex and brought together when wired. The other type has its terminals at the rear and accessible by removing an end cap. Both are available in 2- and 3-pin versions.

Split connector

Remove the two bolts securing the two halves together. Split open and disconnect the flex wires from the terminals of the socket tubes. Lift off the grommet and pull out the old flex. Thread in the end of the

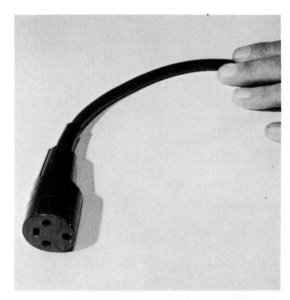

Connecting a flex to a kettle connector. This is a 3-pin kettle connector. The three cores of the flex are connected to the appropriate terminals as shown in the top illustration. In the lower picture the terminal cover has been replaced and the connector is now ready for use

new flex and strip off the sheath for a few inches using the old flex as a guide. Bare the ends and connect them to the respective terminals. Lay the wires in the slots of the halves. Place the other half on top of the one containing the wires and secure the two halves together with the two screws and nuts.

With some patterns of split connector, the earth core is passed through a hole in one half of the moulding and secured under an earth contact strip. This is one of two contact strips which make a rubbing contact with the metal shroud of the kettle to earth the kettle body.

One-piece connector

To wire this type of kettle connector, re-move the screws securing the end cover, loosen the terminal screws and pull out the old flex. Then thread in the new flex, strip the ends and connect the wires to the res-pective terminals. Replace the end cover and fit the plug on the other end of the flex.

Fitting a new connector

If the existing kettle flex connector is in a poor state of repair you should also buy a new connector. The flex is connected by one of the methods described above, but it is best to buy a connector with the flex already fitted.

When fitting a new element to a kettle it is likely that you will also have to get a new connector (and flex) because the existing connector will not fit the element.

Fitting plugs

Most plugs in use in the home today are of the 13 A fused variety having flat pins. There are also many round pin plugs still in use. These are of various current rating and have different sizes of pins, some with three pins, some with only two pins.

The construction of the plugs is fairly standard with the flex entering the plug at the side, though some round-pin plugs have end entry flexes.

Wiring 13 A fused plugs

To wire a 13 A plug, remove the screw securing the cover to the plug base and lift

off the cover. Loosen, or remove the screw of the cord grip and loosen the terminal screws. Place the end of the flex on to the plug base and estimate the length of sheath to remove for the wires to be inserted into the terminals; the wires should lie loosely in the grooves and the end of the sheathing to be clamped under the cord grip.

In some versions of plug, the wires may have to be of different lengths, the earth wire usually being the longest so allow for the longest wire. In other versions, the wires can be all of the same length. Now strip off the required length of sheathing and if necessary cut each wire to length.

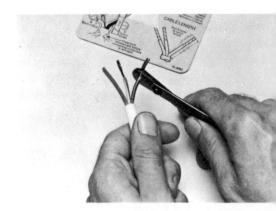

Connecting a flex. (1) Cable ends cut to the same length The insulation is stripped back 9/16 th of an inch (15 mm) ready for inserting into the MK Safetyplug

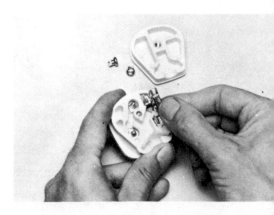

(2) Removing the fuse, prior to insertion of the cables

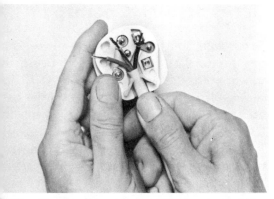

(3) Pressing cables down into the cord grip prior to placing cable ends in position

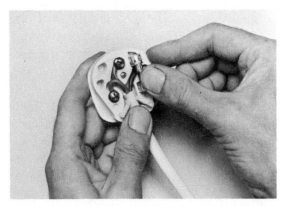

(6) Replacing the fuse into the fully wired Safetyplug. Correct fuse should always be used

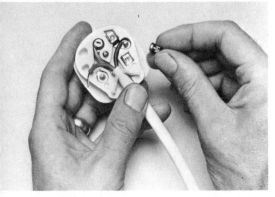

(4) Green/yellow cable (centre) fixed to earth; brown cable (right) being fixed to live; blue cable (left) ready to be connected to neutral

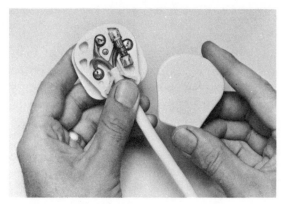

(7) Placing cover on to the Safetyplug

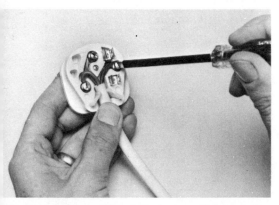

(5) Final check on the terminal screw. The cord grip helps to prevent cable being pulled out of plug which can cause shorting at the ends of the terminals

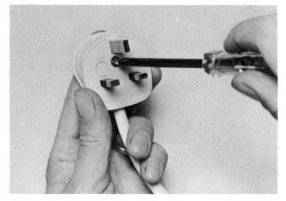

(8) Securing the cover screw. The plug is now ready for use

These photographs are the copyright of MK Electric Ltd, and are reproduced here by permission

Strip off about 15 mm of insulation from the end of each wire. Connect the green/yellow wire first, this to the earth pin terminal, then the brown wire to the live (L) terminal, and finally the blue wire to the neutral (N) terminal. Position the sheath under the cord grip and tighten the screws. Then place the wires into the slots, replace the fuse and the plug cover and tighten the cover screw. Some patterns of plug have two screws but these are now no longer available.

Wiring round pin plugs

Round pin plugs are generally of the same pattern as 13 A flat pin plugs except they do not contain a fuse. The flex is side entry and the cord grip is similar. Some patterns have end entry holes for the flex and are sometimes more difficult to wire depending on the type of flex and its overall size.

The different current ratings of the plugs — 2 A, 5 A and 15 A — are used for the different appliances. The 2 A plugs are used mainly for table lamps and floor standards. The 2-pin plug and the 2-pin socket are largely obsolete but the 2 A plug is suitable for all-insulated and double insulated lamps and appliances fitted with 2-core flex.

In no circumstances may a 2-pin plug be connected to 3-core flex as this would mean leaving the essential earth wire unconnected.

Plugs with double-insulated appliances

A double-insulated appliance, stamped with a double-insulated double hollow square, is fitted with 2-core flex by the makers and has no facilities for earthing.

A flex renewal must also be 2-core. When connecting the 2-core flex to a 13 A fused plug the earth terminal of the plug is left blank.

Screwless cord clamps

The sheath of the flex must always be secured to the cord clamp of the plug as shown in the illustration.

One pattern of plug (made by MK) has no screws to the clamp. Instead the sheath is pressed into the nylon clamp which grips the cord. This design has the advantage that the greater the strain placed on the flex the tighter the grip of the clamp.

Connectors for flexible cords

Generally flexible cords should not be jointed. A flex should be as short as practicable and where an extra length is required temporarily a proper extension lead consisting of the flex, trailing socket and mains plug should be used. Ideally this should be a reel of flex with the socket mounted on the reel.

There are however occasions where a flex needs to be lengthened. In this case a purpose-made connector must be used which is electrically sound and mechanically strong with cord grips to prevent the flex being pulled out of its terminals when under strain.

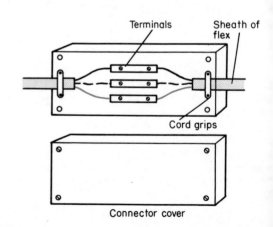

Method of joining two pieces of flex using a flex connector

There are three forms of flex connector for jointing: (i) single-piece connector; (ii) two-section connector; and (iii) line-cord switch. These are described below.

Single-piece connector

This is a line-cord joint box comprising a base containing either two or three terminals, cord grips and a cover secured by screws. The 2-terminal version is for joining two lengths of 2-core flex, the 3-terminal for jointing two lengths of 3-core flex.

Two-section connector

This is a line-cord 3-pin plug and socket with the centre pin (the earth connection) offset to conserve polarity and so preventing reversal. This is essential so that the live wire is connected to the switch of an appliance. The socket section is marked 'mains' and must be connected to the mains length of flex. The plug section must be connected to the appliance flex. The connections are shown in the illustration.

Line-cord switch

The principal purpose of a line-cord switch is to enable a table lamp or an appliance, such as an electric mower, to be switched off and on when in use. It is also a suitable flex connector where a flex is to be extended permanently.

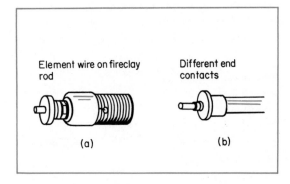

Element wire on fireclay rod

Different end contacts

(a)   (b)

Electric heater elements are made in a variety of lengths, wattages and having different end caps. These are examples of a pencil rod element and a silica enclosed rod element

Line cord switch used as a flex connector. Similar switches are available for 3-core flex

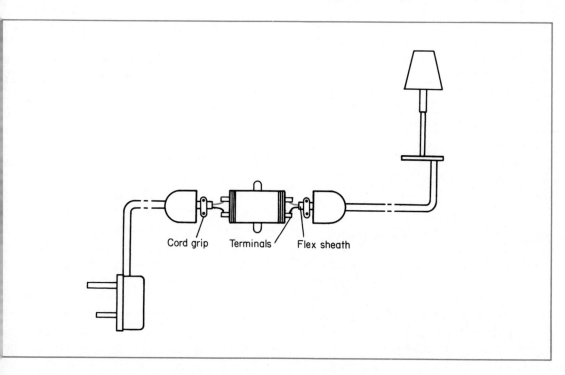

Cord grip   Terminals   Flex sheath

The pear-shaped type used for table lamps and bedhead lamps is a single-pole switch and also has terminals for the through neutral wire. The version used for other appliances is usually a double-pole switch.

Jointing old and new flexes

When an extension flex is to be jointed to the flex of an existing appliance, the flex of the existing appliance will usually have the old code colours of red (live); black (neutral) and green (earth). New flex will have the colours brown (live); blue (neutral) and green/yellow (earth). It is most important to ensure that the green is connected to the green/yellow, the red to the brown and the black to the blue.

This is simple to remember with the fixed connector and the line-cord switch, but is not so simple with the 2-section connector where the terminals are marked L, N and E.

Appliance repairs

In addition to renewing flexible cords there are other repairs within the capability of the householder. These include replacing faulty elements.

Before carrying out any repairs to an appliance first pull out the plug, or in the case of a fixed appliance supplied from a fused connection unit, remove the fuse. If the appliance is not supplied through a fused outlet, turn off the power at the mains.

Repairs to electric fires

Radiant electric heaters have either rod elements or flat bar elements. Convectors and other heaters operating at 'black heat' have special elements which are either open wire spiral elements, sheathed elements, or are totally enclosed.

Rod elements

Conventional electric reflector fires have pencil elements consisting of a wire wound ceramic rod and exposed to touch. 'Infra-red' radiant reflector fires have spiral wire elements enclosed in a silica tube. Each type is made in a variety of lengths, watts loading and with a variety of end contacts. A replacement element must be identical to the original and designed for the make and model of heater. A rod element is attached to the heater either by spring clips or is secured by milled or hexagon nuts.

To remove a pencil type element, it is usually only necessary to release the dress guard, and detach the element from its contacts. If this is of the screw type contact, you loosen the milled or hexagon nut. If the end contacts are enclosed in shields, the shields have to be removed before the element can be taken out.

Silica-enclosed elements

The end contacts of silica-enclosed rod elements are enclosed in shields which have to be released before you can check the type of end contact and measure the length of the element for replacement. Normally the complete element is replaced, though if the silica tube is in good condition, this can be rewired with a new spiral.

Cleaning the reflector

Before fitting a new rod element clean and polish the reflector so that it will operate at maximum efficiency. The reflector is cleaned with soap and water; if chrome, you can use a chrome polisher, subject to the advice of the manufacturer.

A dirty reflector does not reduce the heat output of the fire. It reduces the reflected heat causing the casing to run hot; this heat being emitted by other means including convected heat which could be lost via the flue of a heater standing in a fire-place.

Fire bar elements

Sometimes termed brick elements, these consist of a spiral wire element laid in para-bolic grooves of a 'brick-shape' former. If not fractured, the former can be rewound but the replacement spiral must be of the same length and the same watts loading of the original.

Removing a bar element usually means taking off a rear panel of the heater though, on some models, there is access from the front after the dress guard is released.

Before removing the securing nuts of the bar, it is necessary to disconnect the current carrying wires. These wires are usually either asbestos covered or are stiff uninsulated wires. Some have ceramic beads so take care not to lose some of the beads when disconnecting the wires. Also make a note of the connections.

Check the insulation of the flex within the heater. If damaged by heat, fit a new flex of the heat resisting type.

Replacing convector elements

Partial dismantling of the heater may be necessary to gain access to the elements. Do not buy a replacement until you have removed the faulty element, as designs change and identical replacements must be fitted.

Pilot lights and fuel effect spinners

A pilot light, whether simply an illumi-nating device or part of a fuel effect unit, is usually removed from a heater by means of a detachable panel. With some types, the fuel effect unit has to be lifted to gain access to the lamp.

Lamps may be either clear or coloured but most types have ordinary bayonet caps (BC). These types are readily available but some models use lights with bi-pin caps which may have to be ordered for the par-ticular model of heater.

When a fuel effect spinner ceases to func-tion the cause is either that the spinner is out of alignment or that the bearing is corroded. Remove the spinner assembly, clean and adjust the bearing.

Safety aspects of illuminating devices

The purpose of a pilot light is to indicate that the heater is in circuit and current carrying parts are live at mains voltage. It is also a visual indication that a heater opera-ting at 'black heat' is consuming electricity.

From the safety aspect, replace a faulty pilot light as soon as possible as, if an ele-ment has burnt out, the contacts though 'cold' will be live with the added risk of an electric shock. Single-element radiant heaters have no integral switch on the heater, un-less the heater is of the fuel effect type. This element serves as a visual indicator and, if it fails, the heater should be taken out of service.

For the same reason one element of a multi-element radiant heater without fuel effect is not switched at the heater but glows when the plug is inserted or the socket-outlet switched on. This element is usually the first to fail as it is the one that is most used. This should also be replaced as soon as it fails.

Radiant fires manufactured subsequent to 1975 are required by statute to be fitted with an isolating switch, so that all live parts can be made 'dead' before handling the elements or when attending to the dress guard.

Switch failures

When a switch on the heater fails it is necessary to order a new one that is identical to the original. If any difficulty arises the heater should be taken to an electrical repair shop.

Electric kettle elements

The immersion heater of an electric kettle is made in a variety of shapes and electrical loadings. The flange of the element also varies with the make and model, some being 3-pin, others 2-pin with spring contacts for earthing the kettle body.

When an electric kettle element fails, the replacement element must be one which will fit that kettle. When buying the new element, either take the old element or the complete kettle. With the replacement element are two flange washers, one rubber and one fibre. You may also need a new flex connector and possibly a new flex. These come in various kits with or without connector and flex.

If your kettle is of the high-speed type having a high loading element then the replacement element must be of this type. If it is a standard (low loading) kettle, you may be able to buy a high speed element to fit it should you so wish.

An automatic kettle has an element which switches off as the water boils. If not attended to, it will switch on and off at intervals with no risk of the kettle boiling dry.

Most standard electric kettles will accept an automatic replacement element so when your element fails you may be able to take the opportunity of converting your kettle to an automatic.

Take your kettle to the local electrical shop so that you can check whether there is a suitable automatic element to replace the old element.

Replacing an element

Proceed as follows:

(i)   Unscrew the flex connector shroud, taking care not to damage it if chromium plated, or fracturing it if moulded plastic.

(ii) Push the flange and pin assembly into the kettle body. If you live in a hard water district it may be necessary to remove the scale around the element before you can ease it into the body.

(iii) Lift the element out through the top of the kettle body.

(iv) Scrape off the scale around the flange hole, inside and outside the body and finish it using fine emery cloth, or glass paper.

(v)   Fit the new rubber washer over the flange of the new element.

(vi) Pass the element into the kettle body, the correct way up, flange first and pass the flange through the flange hole.

(vii) Fit the fibre washer on to the flange and replace the connector shield.

(viii) Tighten the connector but do not use a wrench which would damage the shroud.

(ix) If you have bought a new connector but not wired to a new flex, connect this to the flex and also the plug.

(x)   Fill the kettle, plug in and check for any leaks at the flange. If leaking, tighten the shroud until the leaking stops.

Electric irons

When the element of an electric iron fails, the iron has to be dismantled to fit the new element. This is sandwiched between a pressure plate and the sole plate. Some

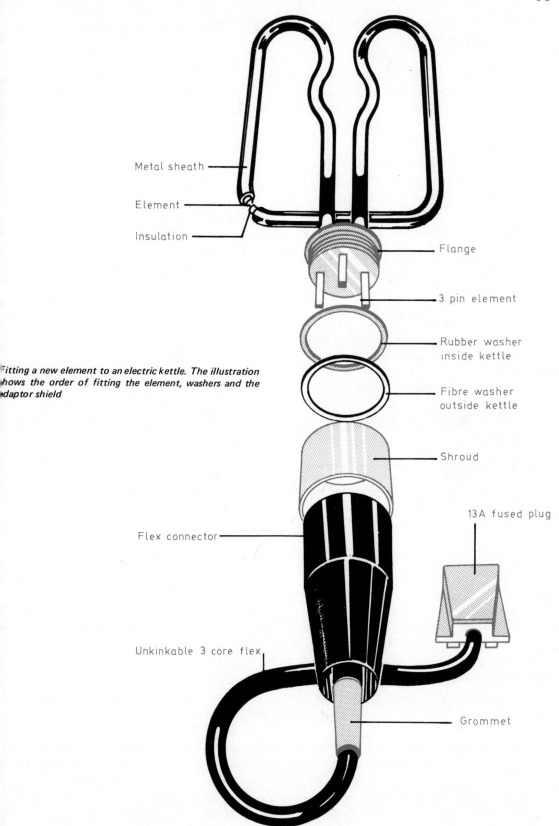

Metal sheath

Element

Insulation

Flange

3 pin element

Rubber washer
inside kettle

Fibre washer
outside kettle

Shroud

13A fused plug

Flex connector

Unkinkable 3 core flex

Grommet

*Fitting a new element to an electric kettle. The illustration
shows the order of fitting the element, washers and the
adaptor shield*

models have the element embedded in the sole plate. When these fail the soleplate is replaced as a unit.

Dismantling a dry or a steam iron should not be attempted without following the manufacturers instructions. If these are not available then the repair should be carried out by the manufacturers.

If the iron overheats, or the sole plate temperature does not correspond to the setting on the dial, the thermostat needs adjusting or replacing. This, too, is a job for the trained mechanic.

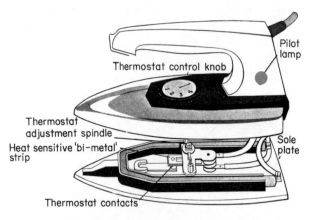

Exploded view of a thermostatically controlled electric iron, showing the sole plate with element and the thermostat contacts and adjusting device to provide variable control of the sole plate temperature

Electric toasters

An automatic (pop-up) toaster has a complicated mechanism. If the toast does not brown correctly the pop-up mechanism needs adjusting. If one side only browns either or both slices of toast, an element has failed. If the toaster does not heat, the fault is usually in the cut-out provided the flex is in order and the plug fuse has not blown.

Check the fuse and the flex, if these are not faulty have the toaster tested at the electrical shop. It is not advisable to attempt to repair the toaster yourself.

Small cooking appliances

Apart from fitting a new flex, small cooking appliances are not easy to repair without the aid of the makers' servicing manuals. If you are unable to obtain these, the appliances should be returned to the electrical shop from which they were bought.

Powered appliances

When the motor of a powered electrical appliance, having a brush-type motor, fails the trouble may be in the brushes.

If the brushes have worn down to less than about 6 mm (¼ in) they need replacing. Replacements are readily obtainable for most appliances but they must be identical replacements. If the fault is not due to the brushes or the motor is of the induction type (having no carbon brushes or commutator) one or more windings or coil may have burnt out. This can usually be detected by a smell of burning. It is best to take the complete machine to the dealer rather than attempt to remove or dismantle the power unit.

Vacuum cleaners

Apart from the flex, the most usual failure of an upright machine is belt breakage or the belt coming off the spindle. If the motor runs erratically accompanied by sparking inspect the carbon brushes and, if worn down to 6 mm, replace them.

Loss of suction is usually traced to the dust bag, or in the hose connections of the horizontal machines. When the motor of a vacuum cleaner produces an unusual noise other than that of increased speed when a belt slips off or breaks, it should be examined by a qualified repairer.

Power tools

These have a similar motor to the vacuum cleaner; the most common fault being brush wear. Burning out of the windings is also fairly frequent and is usually caused by overloading due to misuse.

Electric mower faults

The popular low-priced rotary mowers are usually powered by a brush motor similar to that of an electric drill (power tool). Carbon brushes need replacing when they wear but the component which is likely to give the greatest concern is the thermal cut-out usually situated in the handle. The function of this is to cut off the current to the motor when there is a risk of overload when cutting very long grass.

The cut-out trips and stops the motor, but will not start again until the motor cools which may be a few minutes. If the cut-out fails then either the cut-out or motor (or both) will burn out and the machine should be taken to the dealer for repair.

If the switch fails you can usually buy a replacement. Dismantle the handle, disconnect and remove the faulty switch. If you sever the flex, either fit a new flex or join it using a proper connector designed for outdoor use.

Large electrical appliances

When major electrical appliances such as washing machines, refrigerators, freezers and cookers break down or fail it is advisable to contact the manufacturers or dealer. It is not advisable to attempt to repair these other than fitting a new flex or replacing a plug fuse.

To replace components, other than those mentioned above, usually means partly dismantling the machine. This requires special tools and the makers' servicing manual which is not made available by the majority of manufacturers.

Know your flexible cords

Flexible cords are made in a variety of types for the various appliances and situations and for lighting fittings. When rewiring a pendant or replacing a worn flex on an appliance you should choose the correct type and size. The types used in the home are listed below and the sizes are given in Table 6 on page 98.

(i) Parallel twin flexible cord

PVC insulated cores of the same colour, usually of opaque white but with distinguishing ribbing or a colour stripe for one core when used with an appliance having a single-pole switch or thermostat which must be connected to the live pole. Applications include small all-insulated and double-insulated appliances such as electric clocks, and also lighting fittings.

(ii) Flat twin PVC sheathed flex

PVC insulated cores, one brown, one blue, enclosed in PVC sheathing of flat cross section. Is fitted to some double-insulated appliances in place of circular sheathed flex.

(iii) Circular braided flex

Vulcanised rubber-insulated cores plus cotton fillers to provide circular cross section enclosed in two-colour cotton braiding. Is fitted to many domestic appliances including, heaters, irons and kettles.

(iv) Unkinkable circular sheathed flex

Rubber-insulated cores and cotton fillers enclosed in a light covering of vulcanised rubber and an overall two-colour braiding. Available in 3-core only and is fitted to electric kettles, percolators, irons and similar appliances.

(v) Circular rubber sheathed flex

Rubber-insulated cores together with fillers enclosed in black or grey vulcanised rubber sheathing. Is fitted to a wide range of appliances especially in situations subjected to fairly wide temperature variations.

(vi) Circular PVC sheathed flex

PVC insulated cores (2- and 3-core) enclosed in moulded PVC in circular cross-section but, being moulded, requires no fillers. It is very robust for indoor and outdoor use and will withstand fairly rough treatment and much flexing without kinking. Is fitted to a large range of indoor appliances in place of circular braided and circular rubber flexes, and also in lighting pendants.

Sheath colours are grey, black, white, orange and safety yellow; these last two are used with mowers and hedge trimmers.

(vii) Heat-resisting flex

A 3-core flex having butyl or EP rubber compound heat-resisting insulation. Is fitted to immersion heaters, water heaters, space heaters and to some lighting pendants.

Table 6 FLEX SIZES AND USES

Core size mm²	Current rating, A	Application
0.5	3	Lighting fittings
0.75	6	Lighting fittings; small appliances
1.0	10	Appliances up to 2000 W
1.25	13	Appliances up to 3000 W
1.5	15	Appliances up to 3500 W
2.5	20	Appliances 4500 W (max)
4.0	25	Appliances 6000 W (max)

Chapter 12
Tools

Many of the tools required for electrical work and repairs are usually those to be found in the home toolbox. Some special tools are needed as also are some instruments for testing.

Small tools for repair work

Tools required for small repairs are as follows:

Small screwdriver.
Medium size screwdriver.
Pair of pliers.
Pair of round nose pliers.
Phillips screwdrivers for Phillips and Posi-drive screws.
Wire stripper.
Sharp knife.
One torch.

Tools for house wiring

Saws:
Tenon saw for cutting floorboards.
Rip saw for cutting tongues from T and G floorboards.
Pad saw and blades.
Hacksaw and blades.
Rawlplug tool and bits.
Power tool and drills (optional).
Carpenter's ratchet brace and bits.
Electrician's ratchet brace (optional) for drilling cable holes in joists.
Hammers:
A 2 lb ball pain hammer for general use.
Medium weight hammer.
Pin hammer for fixing cable clips.

Wood chisels:
One 1 in chisel.
One ½ in chisel.
Cold chisels:
One small diameter 6 in chisel.
Two 12 in chisels for lifting floorboards.
Two electricians's bolster chisels for floorboard lifting, cutting chases in walls for cables and flush boxes for switched socket-outlets and other wall mounting wiring accessories.
One bradawl for piercing holes.
One pair of pipe grips for tightening cable glands.
One pair of gas pliers for tightening brass bushes in conduit boxes.
One steel tape.
One ruler.
A straight edge — this could be a straight length of timber — for marking cable runs.
One chalk line and plumb line weight for marking cable runs.
One small spirit level.
One small trowel for making good breaks in plaster.

Instruments required for testing

For testing you basically need only a neon screwdriver, a test lamp and a continuity tester.

Neon screwdriver

A neon screwdriver has a small neon lamp in the handle. When the tip of the blade comes into contact with a live terminal or wire, the neon light glows. This tells you that the terminal or wire is in the live pole of the circuit. It will also indicate that the unearthed metal frame of an electrical appliance is live to touch.

Test lamp

A test lamp is simply an electric light bulb in a lampholder with two leads connected to the lampholder terminals. It should be fitted with a wire guard. This is used to test whether there is electric current at a ceiling rose, socket-outlet or joint box.

Continuity tester

A continuity tester tests whether a fuse has blown, whether a wire has a break in it and the electrical continuity of the earth wire and earthing. The tester can be a sophisticated instrument or it can be constructed with a battery, torch bulb and bulb holder.

Further helpful reading

Beginner's Guides are pocket-sized but contain an enormous amount of information of interest to DIY enthusiasts from novices to old hands who insist they are well past the 'beginner' stage!

For example, **Beginner's Guide to Domestic Plumbing** gives clear, concise coverage, with detailed illustrations, of all that the householder needs to know about domestic plumbing design and materials, the techniques of hot and cold water supply, sanitary installations and drainage. For those easily baffled by electrics, **Beginner's Guide to Electric Wiring** is an easily readable yet authoritative guide requiring no previous technical knowledge. It covers the planning and installation of wiring accessories and fittings in the home and workshop — always with the emphasis on safety and conformity with the Wiring Regulations. If you want to produce well-finished woodwork, **Beginner's Guide to Woodworking** is an introduction to this satisfying craft that will increase both theoretical knowledge and practical skill. It describes clearly the tools and methods used by professional carpenters and joiners, so that the reader can put into practice their basic techniques.

For the more ambitious do-it-yourselfer, **Beginner's Guide to Building Construction** introduces the principles of construction, providing the knowledge that is essential for making a success of any building job, whether a small home extension or a complete structure, from the foundations to the roof and drains.

Fuel and power costs are an increasing worry for every householder. **Beginner's Guide to Home Energy Saving** gives down-to-earth-guidance on minimising the bills. Possibilities described range from no-cost 'energy housekeeping' measures to investments, large and small, in insulation and other improvements — not forgetting possible snags and side-effects. **Beginner's Guide to Central Heating** provides an understanding of central heating in its many forms, so that both intending owners and existing owners whose heating equipment needs replacing can choose the most effective and economical system. The author also gives advice on efficient heating control.

These are all available from bookshops. For further information please write to:

Newnes Technical Books
Borough Green, Sevenoaks, Kent TN15 8PH

Chapter 13
A guide to lighting fittings

Although the primary purpose of a lighting fitting is to provide light, a fitting is exposed to view throughout the hours of daylight and it is, therefore, equally important that it is pleasing to look at when not alight. Before buying a fitting decide whether you would prefer a ceiling fitting or wall lights. If you decide on a ceiling fitting choose between a pendant or a close-mounted ceiling fitting.

Also, decide on the position of the fitting as this will also affect the choice. When choosing in the shop or department store try and visualise how a fitting would appear in your home. This is not easy when the shop has a forest of fittings, some alight and others unlit.

Planning a lighting scheme

If planning a lighting scheme from scratch you should still plan it on a room basis and in conjunction with the furnishing scheme. Remember too that panel lighting, alcove lighting, table lamps and floor standards all contribute to the quantity of lighting and will influence your choice of fittings.

Spotlights, too, have become increasingly popular but do not overdo it. Choose these later if they are to be supplementary to the main lighting to illuminate fabrics or features in a room. Also consider fluorescent lighting, but be careful with the

colour rendering of different tubes or you could ruin your decorative scheme during the hours when the lights are switched on.

Types of fitting

Lighting fittings cover a vast range of types and styles with new fittings being added almost continually. The choice is therefore wide.

Lighting fittings cover five main types: Pendants; close-mounted ceiling fittings; wall lights; spotlights and bulkhead fittings.

Pendant fittings

The simplest and most commonplace pendant is the plain pendant, which is just a ceiling rose and a lampholder suspended by a flexible cord. It covers a majority of lighting fittings in the home and is made in various styles, all of which are basically similar.

Plug-in ceiling rose

A break from the conventional, is the 'plug-in' ceiling rose which has 3-pin socket as a base and a 3-pin plug for the flex connection. This assembly is contained in a moulded plastic ceiling rose cover resembling that of a conventional ceiling rose. Its function is to simplify wiring the flex and allows the pendant to be detached for cleaning.

Detachable ceiling plate

Another but similar type, is a metal plate carrying the flex which slides into the fixed portion. In addition to the cord grip type, versions are available having either a chain hook for a heavy-weight fitting or fitted with a rod for rod suspension. The function of this type is to facilitate cleaning and maintenance of the lighting fitting.

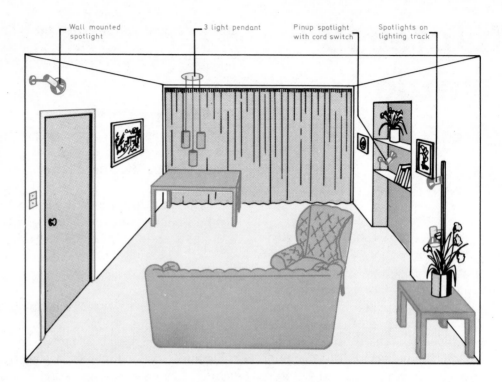

Lighting fittings for a living room

Single light pendants

Apart from plain pendants, single light pendants are made in various styles and types with flex, chain or rod suspension and a variety of shades and diffusers.

Rise and fall pendants

Of more unusual interest is a rise and fall pendant enabling the height of the light, suspended by the sheathed flex, to be adjusted as required. One application is in the dining room over the dining table. As the light unit is raised the flex winds into the rise and fall unit in the ceiling plate. Matching fixed-height pendants are also available. The rise and fall principle is a development of the old rise and fall pendant operated with a system of pulleys and ballast weights.

Accent lights

This is a term applied to a range of low-level long-flex single-light pendant fittings in various colours containing a reflector lamp. These produce pools of light to put a fresh accent on coffee tables and on individual room features. They are available in a fixed version as well as the rise and fall version, with matching wall light versions.

Multi-light pendants

The main choice here covers 2- 3- and 4-light fittings as well as fittings having large numbers of small powered lamps including candle lamps. Conventional bulbs burn in the 'cap-up' or the 'cap-down' position and some have both 'cap-up' and 'cap-down' burning bulbs.

Switch control

Any multi-light fitting can be switched by more than one switch. This means that when choosing a multi-light pendant you are not committed to having all bulbs in use when you switch on the light.

Close-mounted ceiling fittings

A close-mounted ceiling fitting is necessary in situations where restricted headroom does not permit a pendant. It is also fitted in the bathroom where a flexible cord is not approved and it must not be possible for a person using the bath to be able to touch a lighting fitting.

Batten lampholder

The batten lampholder is the simplest and cheapest close-mounted fitting. It can be used with or without a shade, but in bathrooms or W.C.s and similar situations, the lampholder should be fitted with a deep HO (Home Office) pattern skirt. This prevents a person changing a bulb making contact with the metal lamp cap while the lamp is in contact with the lampholder pins. In addition to the straight batten lampholder, there are angle lampholders for fixing in situations with very little headroom or where the lamp projection is to be at a minimum. More recent developments are a swivel batten lampholder and an adjustable angle lampholder (see page 76).

Enclosed fittings

Totally-enclosed close-ceiling fittings have either a glass or a plastic light diffuser and are intended mainly for bathrooms, kitchens and similar situations including a weatherproof version for fixing out of doors. There is also a decorative range for living rooms including a range having crystal glass diffusers and also circular fluorescent fittings with the circular tube enclosed in attractive diffusers of various patterns and colours.

Some circular fluorescent fittings have an external tube with the diffuser inside the circle and mounted flush with the tube.

Downlighters

Downlighters are ceiling fittings of tubular shape alloy containing reflector bulbs or spotlights to produce pools of light on the table and floor against a dark ceiling background. They can be mounted as close-ceiling fittings but there are also versions for sinking flush with the ceiling and some are semi-recessed. The flush version, and to a lesser extent the semi-recessed version require a deep void above the ceiling.

Wallwashers

These fittings are also mounted flush with the ceiling but instead of producing pools of light on the horizontal plane, produce them on walls as part of a lighting scheme. Colour lamps and coloured walls produce the required effect.

Wall lights

Wall lights are made in single lamp and in multi-lamp versions and are available as matching accessories to the main lighting fittings.

Wall lights are available with and without integral press-button or cord-operated switches. Those having integral switches are chosen where it is desired to be able to switch individual lights on and off as required. These should be master switched by a circuit switch, as must the switchless type.

Slide-on wall lights

A range of wall lights from one manufacturer has a novel backplate enabling the fitting to be detached from the fixed backplate by sliding action. The connection between the circuit wires and the wires of the fitting is by a plug and socket arrangement.

Spotlights

A spotlight, and its associated floodlight is a special lamp or bulb having an internal reflector and mounted on a swivel bracket fitting. The fitting housing the lampholder is in various styles and colours to match the decor or to provide a pleasing effect. The lamps are made in various wattages and colours.

Sealed beam spotlights and floodlights, termed PAR 38 lamps, are intended principally for outdoor use in waterproof lampholders. These allow immersion in the garden pool but they are also being used increasingly inside the home either as supplementary or as main lighting for a room and also for discos.

Although it is basically a lighting system rather than fittings, trunking is used to provide a flexible lighting system using mainly spotlights.

Porch light fittings

The lighting fitting for the porch can be a close mounted ceiling fitting, a pendant fitting or a wall mounted light.

Close mounted fittings are mainly enclosed diffuser fittings which can also be mounted on the wall. Pendant fittings are chiefly lanterns suspended by a chain but there are many styles of pendant which can be installed in the porch where not exposed to the rain.

Wall lights are also available in lantern form; a popular unit being an imitation coach lamp.

Front porch fittings are available bearing the number or name of the house in various styles of letters or figures.

Weatherproof fittings

Outside lighting fittings exposed to rain and snow are of weatherproof construction. These are mainly bulkhead fittings or totally enclosed fittings mounted on brackets including angle brackets for corner mounting.

Chapter 14
Control of lighting and heating

Lighting in the home is controlled mainly by conventional switches fixed to the wall and operated by a dolly or a rocker which switches the light on and off. Some lights such as those in bathrooms, over the bed-head and in similar situations are controlled by cord-operated ceiling switches.

Both wall and ceiling switches are of the one-way type for single switch control, two-way for controlling a light from two different positions, and intermediate switching for controlling a light from three or more positions. The circuits for these switching arrangements are described in Chapter 3.

Two other forms of control are dimmer switches and time-lag switches.

Dimmer switches

A dimmer switch enables the light from an ordinary electric light bulb to be varied from full brilliance down to a mere glow. It is an electronic device consisting of a thyristor (or triac, which is a kind of transistor), a printed circuit and associated components. Unlike a wire wound resistor, it consumes an insignificant quantity of electricity and represents a saving in electricity even though a bulb operates at a lower efficiency at lower brilliance. By turning down the light less electricity is used though saving electricity is not the primary purpose of installing dimmer switches.

Types of dimmer switch. The top illustrations show a conventional dimmer switch giving easy control of room lighting. The centre picture shows a combined dimmer and on/off switch. A two-gang dimmer switch for controlling two lights independently from one position is shown in the lower picture

The dimmer switch is styled to match the ordinary electric light switch and as it has a standard-size faceplate it will fit the standard switch mounting box in both flush and surface versions. The dimmer can therefore replace the modern plate switch without changing the mounting box or modifying the wiring.

The dimmer switch is made in various patterns depending on the make. The majority have a rotary knob, but some have a milled edge control, whilst others have a slide control. The dimmer switch is suitable for controlling any home lighting using filament lamps, i.e. the main lighting in the living room; wall lighting; bedroom main lighting or bedhead fixed lighting; the light on the landing or in the hall. It can also be used as a night-light when required in a child's bedroom.

A dimmer switch has a maximum rated wattage, usually 200 W, 300 W or 500 W. Versions are available having ratings up to 5000 W. The 500 W version is commonly used in the home enabling multi-light fittings and groups of lights to be controlled by the one dimmer without risk of damaging it by overload.

Dimmers usually have a minimum watts rating below which they will not operate. This is usually 40 W which means that you would not use it to control a single 15 W or 25 W bulb. Where you have a light containing a small bulb you wish to control by a dimmer you can fit a higher wattage bulb.

Dimmers for 2-way switching

A more recent introduction is a dimmer switch for replacing a 2-way switch. Formerly it was necessary to fit a dimmer in addition to the conventional 2-way switch in a 2-way switching circuit.

This dimmer switch has an on/off switch housed in the same assembly as the dimmer and mounted on the same faceplate. The combination is usually a rocker switch and the dimmer control knob or slide situated side-by-side. Some makes have a single knob which provides on/off control by press-button action and rotating the knob provides the dimmer control.

The combined dimmer and on/off switch is also used for one-way control. The on/off switch enables the light to be switched on and off without disturbing the setting of the dimmer.

Combined dimming and fixed intensity switching

The combined dimmer and on/off switch has yet another function. The dimmer is used to control some of the lighting in a room and the switch is used to control lighting at fixed intensity. From the one switch, therefore, you can have a centre light under dimmer control and wall lights in the same room switched on and off at fixed intensity entirely independent of the centre light, or vice versa.

In a large lounge having a dining recess, you can have the lounge section of the lighting, centre light, or wall lights, under the control of the dimmer and a rise and fall light over the dining table switched at fixed intensity.

Multi-gang dimmers

Dimmer switches are also made in multi-gang assemblies, similar to those of conventional switches. A 2-gang unit is mounted on a one-gang plate for mounting on a one-gang box and will cover most home requirements.

Assemblies of 3-gang and more are mounted on larger plates and require larger mounting boxes. These are mainly used in applications other than the home.

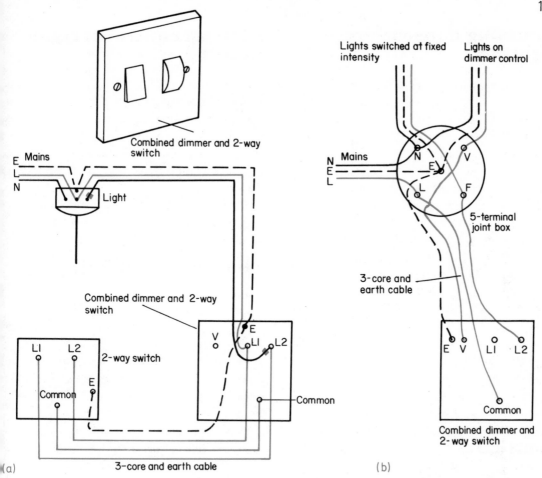

Combined dimmer and 2-way switch

Mains

Light

Combined dimmer and 2-way switch

2-way switch

L1 L2

Common E

V E L1 L2

Common

(a)   3-core and earth cable

Lights switched at fixed intensity   Lights on dimmer control

Mains

N
E
L

5-terminal joint box

3-core and earth cable

E V L1 L2

Common

Combined dimmer and 2-way switch

(b)

Circuit wiring for (a) a combined dimmer and on/off switch and (b) when used to control dimmed lighting and fixed intensity lighting independently

Dimming portable lighting

Table lamps, floor standards, bedside lights and other portable lights can have dimmer control using any one of three methods. One method is a dimmer socket adaptor which plugs into the standard 13 A socket-outlet. This unit has two 2-pin sockets and is especially suitable for controlling two bedside lamps in a twin-bedded or a double-bedded room. The control knob on the adaptor dims both lamps at the same light intensity; they cannot be controlled independently.

Another method uses a line-cord dimmer which is wired into the flex of the lamp. The dimmer can be a standard wall type mounted on a plastic box and placed on the arm of the chair, table, desk, or any other chosen position. Alternatively, it can be a mini-dimmer switch resembling a torpedo table lamp switch. This type is especially suitable for the individual control of bedside lamps.

The third method uses lampholder dimmer which fits most patterns of table lamps and floor standards. With this type of dimmer you 'turn down' the light as one turns down the wick of the old oil lamp.

Yet another method uses the plug-in 'Mood-setter' dimmer as produced by MK Electric Ltd.

Dimming fluorescent lighting

The ordinary dimmer switch is designed for controlling tungsten filament lighting only—electric light bulb, spotlights, architectural tubes, filament striplights, candle lamps and all other forms of filament lighting. Under no circumstances must this type of dimmer be wired into a fluorescent lighting circuit. To do so would damage the dimmer switch beyond repair.

For dimming fluorescent lighting, a purpose-made dimmer is required, as well as a special choke in the fluorescent fitting. An extra wire has to be run from the dimmer to the lighting fitting. Dimming is rarely applied to fluorescent lighting in the home. It is usually better to have auxiliary tungsten lighting in the same room and to control this by a dimmer.

Dimming striplights and spotlights

Tungsten-filament striplights are treated for the purpose of dimming exactly the same as wall lights, using the wall mounted dimmer as a master switch irrespective of whether or not the strip lights have integral switches.

Where spotlights are fitted with flexible cord for connection to a plug and socket-outlet and are to be controlled by a dimmer you can use the socket adaptor type of dimmer. It is essential to make sure that the total wattage of the spotlights does not exceed the watts rating of the dimmer. If one spotlight is supplied from one socket-outlet, there is no risk of overload.

Spotlights, which are expensive to replace, will last much longer when operated at lower output from a dimmer switch but do not sacrifice effect merely to save on lamp replacement.

Dimmer control of track lighting

Lighting tracks consisting of an alloy track which will accommodate a number of spotlights. Track lighting is being increasingly used in the home and is usually connected to the fixed wiring. When ceiling mounted this type can be fitted with a cord-operated switch.

If dimming is required, a wall type dimmer of adequate watts rating is used.

Time delay switching

There are a number of situations in the home where it is useful to be able to control a light by a time lag switch, which will switch off a light automatically after a given interval. Examples include: the hall light, the landing light, outside the back door, in the front porch and similar situations.

A simple time lag switch is a vacuum-operated press-button device which fits the standard plate switch mounting box and will therefore replace any switch without changing the box or altering the wiring. The button is pressed to switch on the light and, after a period ranging from a few seconds to several minutes, the button pops out and the light switches off.

The period of delay is preset by means of an adjusting screw located behind the plate and cannot be tampered with without removing the switch from its box.

The time lag setting, within the limits of the model, should be fixed to suit the situation, bearing in mind that a light will switch off virtually without warning, which could be inconvenient and in some circumstances dangerous. For example, if the light suddenly went out when someone was descending the stairs an accident could result. A time lag switch suitably adjusted is excellent for providing a light in the

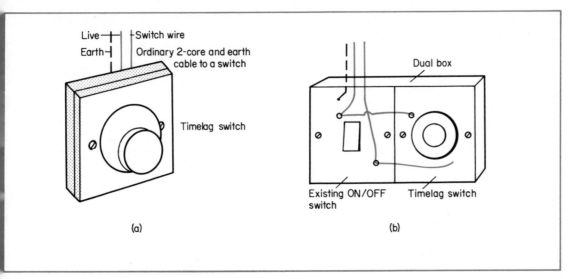

Live — Switch wire
Earth — Ordinary 2-core and earth cable to a switch

Timelag switch

Dual box

Existing ON/OFF switch   Timelag switch

(a)   (b)

A time lag switch. (a) replaces a conventional 1-way switch. (b) wires in parallel with an existing 1-way switch and both mounted on a dual box

porch as you leave the house, go to the car or lock up for the night and in many similar circumstances. Timers providing random switching periods are also available.

Control of heating

Portable electric heaters and many fixed electric heaters are controlled by a switch or switches mounted on the frame of the heater. In addition, the heater is switched at a switched socket-outlet or switched fused connection unit or is connected to a non-switched socket-outlet which means pulling out the plug to switch off the heater.

Integral thermostat

Wall panel heaters, oil filled radiators, convectors and other heaters operating at 'black heat' have an integral thermostat which is set to the required room temperature.

Room thermostats

Where a heater has no integral thermostat, thermostatic control can be arranged by wiring a room thermostat into the circuit. Where the heater is supplied from a socket-outlet, such an arrangement is not practicable. Instead a plug-in thermostat is used, (see below).

If a fixed heater is supplied from a fused connection unit, even when supplied from the ring circuit, a room thermostat can be wired into the heater circuit as shown in the illustration. If, therefore, you have a fixed heater supplied from a socket-outlet on the ring circuit you can control it by a room thermostat by replacing the socket-outlet with a fused connection unit.

Plug-in thermostat

A plug-in thermostat is a very convenient means of providing automatic control for an electric heater. It can be used at any socket-outlet and, like the heater, can be taken from room to room, it not being

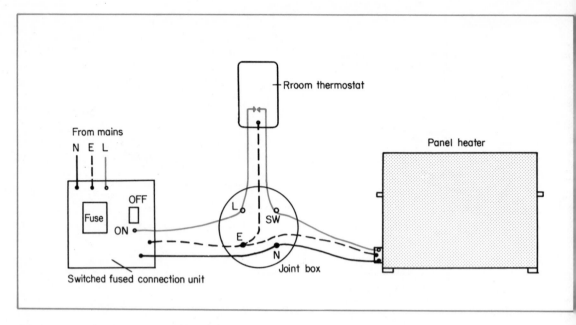

The wiring circuit for a panel heater supplied from a switched fused connection unit wired into the ring circuit and controlled by a room thermostat

necessary to have one for each room. There are a number of models available all of which have an integral socket-outlet for plugging in the heater.

It is not recommended that radiant electric fires are controlled by a thermostat. Apart from being unsatisfactory, the sudden switching on of a radiant portable fire is potentially dangerous.

A plug-in time switch used for individual control of a heater and a matching plug in thermostat also for the individual control of any one heater. By plugging one unit into both, facilities are provided at one socket outlet

Time switches

A time switch is another form of control for electric heaters. It can be used as the sole means of control or it can be used in conjunction with a thermostat. One time switch of adequate capacity wired into a heater circuit can supply a number of electric heaters enabling a whole system of background heating to be switched on and off automatically as required. Alternatively, single heaters can be supplied from time switches each wired into the circuit.

Plug-in time switches

There are also available plug-in time switches, which like plug-in thermostats, can be used to control portable electric heaters. These too should be restricted to convectors and other heaters operating at 'black heat'. It is not advisable to control radiant electric fires from time switches.

Setting the time switch

Most time switches are provided with two switch ON periods and two switch OFF periods per 24 hours; these times being set by the user. There is also a time switch having facilities for three switch ON and OFF periods each 24 hours.

A useful arrangement of switching for background heating is as follows. First switch ON about an hour before the family get up in the morning and then switch OFF as the family leaves for work. The second switch ON about an hour before the first of the family returns home and the final switch OFF during late evening.

Over-ride switch

An over-ride switch is usually incorporated into the time switch to enable the heater,

A single wall mounted panel heater supplied from a switched fused connection unit and controlled by a wall mounted time switch

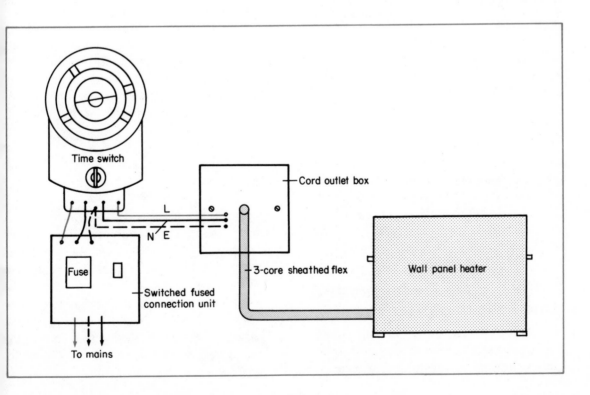

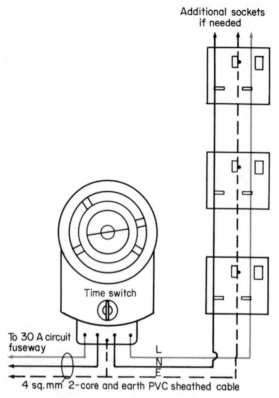

Additional sockets
if needed

Time switch

To 30 A circuit
fuseway

L
N
E

4 sq.mm 2-core and earth PVC sheathed cable

A radial power circuit providing time switch control of a number of panel heaters used for background heating. Switched fused connection units may be used instead of socket outlets

or heaters to be used out of programmed hours without upsetting the time switch setting. When the time switch has no over-ride switch, a suitable switch of the correct current rating can be wired into the circuit. This switch can be of 20 A, 30 A, or 45 A and should have a pilot light as a warning that the heating is under manual control with the time switch temporarily inoperative until the over-ride switch is turned off. switch is turned off.

Combined thermostat and time switch control

The principal function of a room thermostat is to maintain a given temperature in a room or rooms. This can be costly, for the

heating is running virtually 'flat out'. To conserve energy and reduce one's electricity bills a time switch can be wired into the circuit as well. A portable thermostat and a portable time switch can be plugged into each other to produce the same result.

The time switch restricts the hours of switch ON and the thermostat prevents the temperature rising above a predetermined level.

Non-storage electric central heating

An electric heating system comprising a number of non-storage panel heaters and/or oil filled radiators is available from a number of makers as a complete package. The heaters (or radiators) are controlled from a central control panel to restrict the heat output though providing adequate warmth in the various rooms.

The most recent development is a combined storage and non-storage heater. The main heating is from the storage block, charged at the overnight cheaper rate. But when this is exhausted during the latter part of the day, the direct acting non-storage heater in the same heating unit is switched on automatically at the control panel.

Zone control

Packaged electric central heating systems which includes zone controllers are also available. These zone controllers provide different switching periods for bedroom and daytime rooms.

A typical zone controller has two time switches. One is used for the bedroom heating to switch on during the night time. The other switches on the heating in living rooms.

Chapter 15
Hints on safety

Most, if not all, people know that mains electricity in the home is lethal. This means that if you come into contact with a live terminal, live wire or metalwork, which because of a fault is charged with electricity, you will receive an electric shock which could be fatal.

Electricity at the mains voltage of 240 V is present at every ceiling rose, lampholder, switch, socket outlet and other outlets. It is also present at every electrical appliance connected to the mains when plugged into a socket outlet and the switched socket is 'ON'.

Every cable and wire of an installation, except the earth conductors, carries electric current at mains voltage, so should you accidentally severe a cable or damage its insulated sheath you are likely to make contact with a live conductor and receive an electric shock. With more than 15 million homes in Britain receiving a supply of electricity from the mains and these having an estimated average of 25 appliances each it may seem surprising that the number of deaths due to electrical accidents per year is usually below 80. Although these are tragic and bring much distress to the families concerned, they are but a tiny portion of the 8000 deaths arising from all accidents in the home each year. This figure usually exceeds the number killed in road accidents. In the main electrical accidents can be regarded as avoidable and are often due to carelessness.

The relatively few deaths from electrocution are due principally to the high quality of cables and wiring accessories which are made to rigid British Standards designed to prevent wires and contacts being exposed to touch when properly installed. As we have seen in the relevant sections of this book, modern switches and other accessories have high quality moulded plastic faceplates whereas older switches have easily removable screw-on covers which expose the terminals.

Socket-outlets and ceiling roses were usually of porcelain which readily fractured and exposed the live terminals. Flexible cords are now sheathed instead of being merely insulated, wiring cables have a tough PVC sheath. Modern mounting boxes, which have replaced the old wood blocks, ensure that the unsheathed ends of cables are totally enclosed in non-combustible material as are the contacts and terminals of the accessories connected to the cables.

Danger from fire

Although deaths from electrocution are relatively rare, the same cannot be said about fire. Many fires in the home have been traced to bad or overloaded wiring, though these do not necessarily result in deaths. In fact many of the fires reported as electrical are caused by fats and oils igniting in cooking utensils left unattended on the cooker. Such fires also occur on gas cookers and although this does not excuse accidents from electric cookers it is necessary to get the right perspective. There are however many fires caused by electricity, which being small and extinguished by householders, have not been reported and do not appear in official reports.

Causes of fire and shock

The principal causes of fire and shock from electrical installations are faulty wiring,

113

the misuse of appliances and using appliances which are no longer safe.

Faults on appliances can usually be eliminated by periodic inspection but the misuse of appliances is within the hands of the householder and his family. Faulty wiring is more complicated but this too can be rectified by periodic inspections.

DIY wiring and safety

The do-it-yourself enthusiast has, in the past, often been blamed for fires and electric shock accidents due to faulty wiring installations and to incorrect procedures being followed.

Although there is some justification for this and the facts have been substantiated by official reports, there is evidence to show that most amateurs are responsible people and take great care when dealing with electricity. It cannot be disputed that the householder carrying out his own work, whether electrical or other forms of home improvement, is likely to be extremely conscientious. The householder having good mechanical aptitude, experienced in doing jobs about the house, using good quality cables and wiring accessories and carrying out the work in accordance with the information in this book, need have no fear that the finished job will be safe and can be expected to pass any inspections and tests carried out by the electricity board when connecting the wiring to the mains supply.

Never add more lights or socket-outlets to circuits or to parts of a circuit than those specified or you will risk overloading a circuit.

In the interests of safety, though with some repetition from the previous chapters the following summarises the principal points which should be observed when carrying out electrical installation work.

Bathrooms

Take particular care in the bathroom where special regulations apply.

Do not install a socket-outlet in the bathroom other than an approved shaver supply unit for a mains voltage shaver.

Do not make provision for using a mains voltage portable appliance. For example do not run a portable electric heater from a socket-outlet situated outside the bathroom i.e. on the landing or in an adjacent bedroom. If the tank cupboard opens into the bathroom and the tank has an immersion heater do not supply it from a socket-outlet (not a good method in any case) which could be used for plugging in a portable appliance.

Do not have open lampholders in the bathroom where the bulb could be removed and a hair dryer or other appliance plugged in.

Ensure that all switches in bathrooms and washrooms are of the cord-operated type (except, of course, a shaver supply unit). Where this is not practicable, ensure such a switch is out of reach of a person using the bath or shower; this may mean fixing the switch outside the bathroom door.

Do not have a lighting fitting situated over the bath where it could be reached by a person attempting to replace a faulty bulb, standing in the bath.

Make sure that lampholders, even when in an enclosed fitting, have a deep (HO) skirt so that it is not possible to touch the metal lamp cap while the lamp is still making contact with live pins.

Pay particular attention to striplights such as are fixed over a shaving mirror. These designed for bathrooms have shielded lampholders so that the lamp caps cannot be touched when replacing a lamp. Flexible cord pendants must not be fixed in a bathroom.

Where appropriate, bond to earth any extraneous metalwork.

Flexible cords

Flexible cords which are the means for connecting portable appliances and lights to fixed wiring are among the most likely source of accidents.

When renewing flexible cords on appliances make certain that the flex used in each instance is of the correct size and type. If too small (conductor size) it will be overloaded and could result in a fire. If of the wrong type there may be a risk of mechanical damage or in high ambient temperatures the insulations may be damaged.

Do not use twisted twin non-sheathed flex for appliances and wherever possible use sheathed flex on lighting pendant fittings. Do not 'repair' frayed flex with insulation tape but replace the flex when showing signs of damage or wear.

Do not run flexible cord under carpets or other floor coverings.

Under no circumstances use flexible cord for fixed wiring.

Do not connect 3-core flex to a 2-pin plug. The latter is used only with all-insulated and double insulated appliances having no earthing facilities.

Use 2-core flex only for double insulated and all-insulated appliances and for appropriate lighting fittings. Where 2-core flex is connected to a 3-pin plug make sure that the two cores (brown and blue or red and black) are connected respectively to the live and neutral pins of the plug, leaving the earth pin without a connection.

Keep flexes as short as possible when connected to domestic appliances and avoid using multi-plug adaptors. These usually result in long trailing flexes, which apart from risk of damage to the sheathing, are a hazard especially to the elderly and the very young.

Do not have the flex of an electric iron, or even of a kettle too short. This will result in undue strain on the flex.

When connecting flex to its plug or to the appliance, ensure that the sheath is well secured under the clamp so that any strain on the flex will not pull the flex from its anchorage and sever the conductors at the terminals.

Take care that a flex does not droop over a radiant electric fire or that a kettle flex does not come into contact with a cooker hot-plate or gas ring.

Handle with care the flex of your vacuum cleaner and do not drag the cleaner along by its flex.

Take care that the washing machine does not run over its flex when moving it about in the kitchen.

Do not extend the flex of your power tool; the plug should always be within reach when using the tool. When you need a longer flex use an extension flex on a drum fitted with a socket-outlet.

Take particular care of the flex when using an electric mower or hedge trimmer. These flexes are usually either orange or safety yellow in colour to reduce the possibility of the mower running over the flex or the hedge trimmer cutting it. The flex tends to get dragged through rose bushes and shrubs and other obstacles which will damage the sheath. You should therefore inspect the sheathing at the end of each mowing or hedgecutting session or if you suspect damage when using these garden tools.

Repairing damaged long flexible cords

If the sheath of these long flexes is damaged, it is practically impossible to effect a satisfactory repair. Unless the damage is near one end you will not wish to sacrifice any of the flex by cutting off a portion. You can obviate this by using a weatherproof fixed connector. This needs to be water resistant where it is likely to be drawn through wet grass. The connector will form an obstacle and will need more care when using the mower or hedge cutter.

Lamps and lighting

Do not fit a high wattage bulb into a shade or fitting designed for bulbs of lower ratings. Some shades give the maximum wattage but if there is no indication, restrict the wattage to 60 W or preferably 40 W. Otherwise overheating may occur and the shade material either melt or ignite. Damage can also be done to the fixed wiring by transference of heat through the lamp-holders; this is particularly the case if it is a close ceiling fitting. Damage can also be done to the flex, if pendant and the flex is not of the heat-resisting type.

Take particular care when replacing a bulb in a wall light if the light is not independently switched. If the light has only an integral cord switch or a press button switch, there is usually no means of knowing whether the switch is ON or OFF when the bulb has failed.

Do not leave lampholders empty for this represents a shock risk. If you have no spare bulb, leave the old bulb in the lampholder.

Do not add flex extensions to a ceiling rose designed for only one flexible cord.

Do not use twin lampholder adaptors for running an appliance from the light. Apart from putting undue strain on the pendant flex the appliance is likely to over-load the lighting circuit.

Electric heaters

Scorching and fire are the principal hazards associated with electric heaters, particularly radiant heaters and all portable electric heaters.

The first rule of safety is to ensure that a radiant heater is fitted with a correct dress guard. Modern heaters are fitted with the approved guard to prevent a person poking a finger through the mesh as well as to prevent fabrics falling on or brushing the elements and catching fire. Radiant heaters not fitted with approved pattern dress guards should be scrapped.

Periodically check that the fixtures securing the guard have not loosened and that none of the wires of the mesh are broken or have become distorted.

Never stand a portable radiant heater, when switched off, against furniture or fabric or place it facing a wall even when the plug is out of the socket. There is always a risk of someone inserting the plug by mistake and causing scorching and possibly a fire.

Replace a broken element without delay for, not only may stray ends or parts of the rod touch the reflector, but a child may insert a metal object or be able to touch the broken end with a finger and receive a fatal shock.

Do not use a radiant fire with an element missing because the live contacts become a potential hazard when the switch is on without the hot element acting as a warning.

Replace a 'dud' lamp of a fuel effect fire as soon as it fails for this also serves as the necessary pilot light and a warning that the flex is live when the plug is in the socket.

Do not attempt to replace an element or remove a dress guard of a fixed heater without first turning off the main switch if the heater is not supplied from a plug and socket enabling the plug to be withdrawn.

Never place clothing or other materials to dry over the grille of a convector heater, fan heater or storage heater.

Do not let fabrics fall on to tubular and skirting heaters for this would cause a build up of temperature result in scorching and possibly a fire. Also do not let curtains come into contact with this type of heater.

Take particular care in the choice and positioning of heaters in a nursery. Babies are likely to throw clothes on to a free standing convector and can be burned by radiant fires even when these mounted on the wall at high level but easily reached from a displaced cot.

Cookers

Always switch off the control before cleaning a cooker even if it is not being dismantled.

Do not let metal cooking foil come into contact with spiral type elements.

Take care if the cooker is mounted on wheels and likely to be interfered with by youngsters.

Never leave fat in a pan unattended on a hotplate and take care with the position of handles of vessels containing boiling liquid in the presence of children.

Do not attempt to remove pieces of broken toast from a toaster using a knife or other metal object. Pull out the plug before releasing the obstruction.

Kettles

Do not stand a switched-on electric kettle on the cooker where the flex is likely to drape over a hotplate.

Always switch off at the socket when filling the kettle and do not leave the flex plugged in with the exposed kettle connector removed from the kettle and lying on the work top or table.

Do not leave a non-automatic kettle switched on when answering a call at the door or the telephone or when 'popping upstairs for a second'.

If you replace a slow standard element by a high-speed element, wait until the kettle boils before leaving the kitchen as you may under-estimate the speed of boiling. All kettles have thermal cutouts, but if yours fails to operate, a serious fire could result if unattended.

Electric blankets

Buy only a blanket having the British Standard Kitemark. It is now an offence for anyone in Britain to sell a blanket not bearing this symbol.

Follow the makers instructions on fitting and using a new blanket and have every blanket inspected by the makers every three years at least.

Get rid of old blankets and cut off the flex so they are unable to be used again.

Never switch on a mains voltage under-blanket when the bed is occupied. An over-blanket may be switched on when the bed is occupied but it must not be used as an under blanket.

Repairs to appliances

Always pull out the plug before repairing or making adjustments to any electrical appliance and where there is no socket outlet, switch off at the mains. Do not attempt any repairs beyond your capabilities and then only in conjunction with makers servicing instructions for other than simple appliances.

Periodically check the cover securing screw of each plug; if the cover comes off as you pull out the plug (or inserted it) you are likely to touch the live terminals.

Index